BLACKPOOL DISTRICT LIBRARIES ACTION RESERVE X

RESERVE STOCK

-8. AUG. 1967

-3. OCT. 1967

D1486423

AUTHOR	CLASS No. FICTION
Mac PHERSON, E+l	RESERVE
TITLE	
HAPPY HAWKERS	BOOK No.
	06603738

This book must be returned on or before the date shown above
LANCASHIRE COUNTY LIBRARY
COUNTY HALL PRESTON

a30118 010099947b

HAPPY HAWKERS

BOOKS BY IAN MACPHERSON

PRIDE IN THE VALLEY
WILD HARBOUR
LAND OF OUR FATHERS
SHEPHERD'S CALENDAR

BY ELIZABETH MACPHERSON

LETTERS FROM A SCOTTISH
VILLAGE

HAPPY HAWKERS

by

ELIZABETH & IAN MACPHERSON

Illustrated by

MILDRED R. LAMB

METHUEN & CO. LTD. LONDON
36 Essex Street Strand W.C. 2

DR/AR
MAY '66

01009994

First published in 1937

✓ x6111780   q

Reprinted 1965 by Cedric Chivers Ltd., Portway, Bath,
to whom the Copyright has been transferred, at the request of
The London & Home Counties Branch of The Library Association

ECM – ANTON HAIN K.G.

Printed in Germany

CONTENTS

HELDON TREE

CULREOCH

INVERTON

ILLUSTRATIONS

HELDON TREE

A

HELDON TREE

Chapter One

WE HAVE BOATS TO BURN

I was miserably unhappy teaching in a dreich Aberdeenshire townlet. Indeed, I never wanted to teach, but there didn't seem anything else to do with my nice expensive Arts degree. Perhaps if I'd landed in any other school things might not have been quite so grim, but it was my luck to go to one of those Leaving Certificate factories of which Scotland is so proud. Ever since I was ten I seemed to have been living with an eye on the calendar for the next exam., and now, with the university behind me, I found myself paid to force a younger generation through all the worry of my own childish days. All that year I felt trapped and desperate, and the nearer it came to the time of the Higher Leaving Certificate exams., the worse it got. An appalling energy drove us all on, children and teachers alike, to reduce all culture, all learning, all loveliness, into 'spotters' for the wretched examinations.

The headmaster's motto was 'not a moment wasted'. Ian and I took it for our own and decided to get married at once even though it was May, the unlucky month. If we waited, as caution bade, until Ian went to Cambridge, took his degree, and found a job, we might wait long enough, for by that time jobs were growing few and far between. He felt like a square peg in a round hole where he was, finishing a two years' job as assistant to the English professor at Aberdeen, but if he went to Cambridge he might find himself a square peg in no hole at all. So we said good-bye to caution. Perhaps that is the best way to greet caution when you are young.

We were lucky, confounding the May-marriage superstition from the very start. We went to Dundee, complete with witnesses, on a fine Saturday in May. Saturday chose itself because I was teaching all week, and marriage is a sacrament which Scotland does not celebrate on a Sunday. We met in Aberdeen at half-past five in the morning in streets as clean and swept as the sky. When we reached Dundee Ian began to think he would not have enough money to pay the lawyer. In his pocket he had a cheque for two guineas, and when he went in fear and trembling into a bank, the banker confounded our ideas of banks by cashing it, even though it was crossed and we were strangers. We've had a specially warm corner in our hearts for Dundee ever since. Then a commissioner of oaths with ophthalmic goitre married us. I'm not sure that he even saw us.

Our boats were burned now with a vengeance. As married women aren't allowed to teach in

Scotland I couldn't continue in my job even if I
wanted to. Ian was not qualified to teach as he
had never gone to the Training Centre. He had
not, as he was supposed to, saved money out of his
salary to take him to Cambridge. We both spent
our money as it came, Ian chiefly, as I must admit,
on a large and devilishly powerful motor - cycle
called a Matchless.

We had no money, but what was worse, we felt
that once we left the jobs we had we were no
manner of use to the world. I think that feeling
really helped us. There is a good deal of elation
about anger, and we were angry that we were so
useless; no one would take us to build or brew; we
could not do double entry (to this day I have to
think a long time before I know what ninepence
from half a crown leaves); no employer in the
world would think twice about us. We ransacked
our brains; it was now late May, our jobs ended in
the following month, and we must make a living
somehow.

I suppose that it was partly reaction against all
the respectability we had around us that set us
thinking of selling dishes through the country. As
soon as we thought of that we began to see how fine
an idea it was and how pleasantly we might make
a living as hawkers. We knew the Highlands
fairly well, and I knew only too well how dishes had
a knack of breaking themselves. People in remote
places cannot dash out to a store to replace their

shattered tea-sets but must wait for their annual visit to the nearest town to do so. I knew, too, how women love pretty ware, in town and country, but you cannot easily buy pretty dishes in the country. All women love drinking tea from china cups just as all women love shelves full of bonny linen with lavender amongst it; but country women are forced to be content with the coarse *pig* ware that hawkers usually carry and exchange for six times its worth in rags and rabbit skins. I was sure there was a market there. Then there was the fun of choosing fine crockery at one's own doors. Half the joy of buying dishes is the choosing, the handling, the comparing of colours. When a woman sends to the store for dishes she loses all that joy.

We were so sure we could make a living selling china that we were prepared to sink all our small capital on setting up as hawkers. We realized quite well that once committed there could be no turning back. If we failed we'd have no help from any one; but we'd not fail. We sat down very seriously to map out our course. We decided right away that we could not, even if we wished, live like the true-blue hawkers. We meant to have all the comfort possible; we meant to carry a much larger stock of dishes than our trade rivals; and of course we meant to depend altogether on our sales. The real hawkers sometimes do a little begging, or trade in scrap metal, or exchange dishes for rags and rabbit skins. We didn't know enough for that, so our business was to be plain straight-forward hawking and, we hoped, selling of dishes.

If we moved through the country with our stock we must have a place to live in and a vehicle to pull our goods from place to place. A horse sounded tempting, but knowing how scattered are Highland communities, we feared that we might not be able to cover enough ground that way. But there were multitudes of motor-buses on every road, and we imagined that there must be plenty of old buses for sale cheaply. A bus would be the very thing for our purpose, because the body could be converted fairly easily into a living-room-cum-store. So in the intervals of teaching and lecturing we wandered into every garage in Aberdeen and into all the china warehouses. The china merchants could scarcely be persuaded into taking us seriously for all our note-books and freshly sharpened pencils. The garages need a new paragraph all to themselves.

They took us seriously enough until we began to talk *Figures*. They began all smiles and facts. 'Here is a nice little job, sir. Speed Six. Done— let me see—Jock! Hey! Jock! was it six or seven thou. she did? Six—at a crawl! I may say we do quite well with this little job.' Then he would lead us to the little job, a monstrous red thing up-holstered inside like a Victorian drawing-room and with as many curtains as a Sultan's harem. Ian would then say, How much? Whereupon the sales-man would assume a stricken look, as if such grossness about his little job pained him inexpressibly. He would turn to another monster and extol its virtues until he was brought up by the same unfeeling question. Finally he would sigh 'A thousand pounds the piece. And dirt cheap.' I would then lead Ian swiftly away.

At times the garage people, when they saw we had no spare thousands, switched lightly to buses they had not just at that moment in stock, as you might say; but they could lay their hands on them —oh, any time within a week. 'Fine little job,' they'd say caressingly about some dilapidated hack lying with broken springs at the back of Bennachie. 'Sweet engine! The bodywork—well, it might require a little—oh, a *very* little attention. But the engine!' here they sank into a blissful silence as they contemplated the perfection of the engine. We would wait politely till the rapture passed and then mention terms.

'Now how would two hundred and forty suit you? Say two hundred and forty and we'll put that bus on the road like new.' When we did not say two hundred and forty, they started to trickle away until they heard us say very firmly *Forty*, at which they retired swiftly to the Olympian fast-nesses of their offices to put their ties straight in front of mirrors taken probably from the buses they were trying to sell us; or else they walked with us to the door, smiling from the teeth out.

It was now well into May and we were beginning

to give up some of our first hopefulness. We made from garage to garage, from china shop to china shop, reckoned our slender purse, and drew up our summer route as well as some very ambitious posters which we meant to squander over the country as we went, but which actually were no sooner born than blasted because we never could afford to have them printed. At this stage we were mightily ambitious. We meant to cover twenty miles a day up Speyside, into Perthshire, round the West Coast, across to the East, and back to the mouth of the Spey. We also planned to decorate our bus with coloured lights so that our very appearance might entertain our prospective customers. Feeling that we ought to have a name, we bought a fresh note-book and printed

AUTOLYCUS LIMITED

over its first page in large capitals. We were so charmed with all the empty pages that we proceeded to fill them up with details as to routes, advertising, furnishing, clothes, tools, like hammers and spades, and details of our expenditure.

Time was passing very fast and it was essential to have everything set so that we could step from our lecturing and teaching right into our new business. I was also very worried at that moment about the Oral examinations, which are the tail-end of the Higher Leaving Certificate exams. So I had perforce to let Ian pursue a solitary way among the garages the whilst I dinned a last-minute survey of English literature into the already dazed and bewildered ears of my pupils. Ian wrote me almost daily of his trials and triumphs. Here is a bit of one of his letters:

—yesterday I met a man very eager to sell a 1926 Essex. The Essex has had a fire in its inside but its engine is good. Of course that's the usual formula of men with battered old wrecks of cars for sale but I know the man who sold it to the man who wants to sell it and the price he got was £7. I offered £12 for it—it's had a few things done to it—but the garage man, he wants Fourteen. He assures me that it's a miracle of speed and stamina and that he'd get about five times what he's asking from me if he sold it for scrap. 'Michty, man,' says he, 'if I was to take the labour to break it up I'd get a quid for the hinner end for a hen coop.'

I'd to go to King's to lecture but I hurried back and offered him £13. He was hitting an old Morris great whacks with a sledge-hammer when I arrived in his yard and he was quite cheerful about having broken his promise not to sell the Essex while I was away. However, he advised me to buy another car he has which, he says, will pull a house. Of course the engine is good! At any rate no other body on earth is likely to buy this fresh car he's offering so we'll go and see it when you come in on Friday——

We duly went to see the other car and discovered her to be the most disreputable Yankee car you ever saw. She looked about thirty feet long, had a touring body, was painted a dirty grey, was called a Chalmers, and had all the leaves in the near front spring broken except two. The garageman hauled her out into the light of day and gave her wheels and body several resounding blows with a hammer much as a horse-dealer smacks a horse's chest. He looked at us triumphantly when the Chalmers didn't cough.

We couldn't see her wonderful engine running because she had battery ignition and the battery was—now where was the battery? He clawed his back with an adjustable spanner. 'Oh, aye,' he said, his brow clearing. 'The battery's in the ice-cream shop across the road, working the wireless.' He smiled another triumphant smile as if we could never go wrong buying a car whose battery was good enough to run a wireless set. The whilst we waited for the battery we contemplated the car. We were dismayed by its horse-power, which was twenty-five. The licence for that would be a heavy load on paupers. Then there was that broken spring. The garage man, it is true, piloted us skilfully past the spring and dilated on the smooth running and docility of this paragon of cars. At last the battery arrived and was fixed up. The engine did sound good. The Chalmers ran as sweetly as a sewing machine and sounded like unlimited power, so we bought her and paid ten of our few pounds for her—about 6s. 11d. the running foot, or one pound and ninepence per yard.

The next business was to get a place to live in. The car could hold our goods, but we knew north-country summers and had no intention of ruining our health and temper by any haphazard camping out. We wanted a caravan, and a good caravan. The man who sold the Essex to the man who sold us the Chalmers knew of a 'real fine' caravan for sale to be had from one George White. He said 'George White' in such matter-of-fact tones that we were ashamed to ask where this man, so obviously known to every one save us, could be found. At this point I had to catch a train back to my teaching, so I left Ian to search for George and the caravan. Tuesday of the following week brought me a letter from my indefatigable husband:

I have found G. W., he said. *He conducts an uproarious business in a quiet side street in Old Aberdeen down amongst the peace of old trees, aged houses, and ancient professors. He has a yard there where he repairs all kinds of traction engines, heavy lorries, and threshing mills. When I got there I found Sentinels and Fodens packed together like herring in a barrel and wondered how on earth they got in, or when they were in, out, until another Foden suddenly appeared snorting at the gate ; the driver bawled at me to move aside, and when I did he came in, Foden and all, and parked in a place where I shouldn't have liked to try to park the motor-bike.*

'Oh, aye, the battery's in the ice-cream shop.'

*I asked him for George White. There was a second's
hush and then every one in the yard let out a collective
bawl for George. 'George!'—They shouted into
the sky, into the cabins of lorries, round great huge
detached wheels, hallooing his name to the reverberate
steam engines, and a little boy whose voice hadn't
broken enough to be worth shouting with ran into the
office and started a great gong of a bell ringing above
the entrance gate.*

*George finally appeared quietly from the street,
and when his men saw him they stared at him for a
moment before they yelled 'Oh, there you are,
George. Man to see you.' And to me 'There he is
now, there's George.'*

*George is a short, broad, fair man and he spake
me so winningly that in five minutes he knew our
business, what we could offer, showed me a receipt
dated the previous autumn for the wood he used to
build the caravan, and told his price as if that was
least of all. He remarked too that the van has a
mollycroft roof whatever that may be, and was so
elder brotherly as to confide that he was born in a
van but had no intention of dying in one yet awhile,
so he made sure they were always built with this
mollycroft roof. He's selling because he has a family
and the van is too small for George plus family.
He swears that it will never leak nor sweat nor be
over-hot in summer nor over-cold in winter. It's
double lined throughout with three-ply wood which
alone cost forty-seven pound ten per receipt already*

shown.   There's a lovely little stove bedded in
asbestos.   It sleeps four, is as light as love, as strong
as death, and along with our car will presumably be
as silent as the grave.   I don't think we can do better.
What do you say?

I said, Go and see this miraculous affair, but Ian
waited till I came in at the week-end before going
to view our future home.   George was waiting for
us when we returned to his yard from inspecting
the van.   'Forty,' said Ian laconically.   George
fondled the huge gold chain on his waistcoat.
'Forty-seven and I'll fix a drawbar on your car.'
'Forty-five and put a drawbar on,' countered Ian.
Whereupon George swung round like a flash and
grabbed Ian's hand.   We paid £30 down and
promised the rest at the end of the month.

'Bring your car on Monday,' George admonished
us, and we walked out of the yard feeling like old
respectable householders.

We have shared many uncomfortable adventures
together, but one which I must confess I was glad
not to experience was that first trip with the
Chalmers through Aberdeen's traffic.   Ian said
afterwards he felt like a man in a nightmare pilot-
ing the *Mauretania* through hotel corridors.   However, he arrived safely at George's yard, to find
George waiting for him.   I expect he was rather
curious about Corybante, as we got to calling the
car.   He walked all round it in a friendly way and
muttered something about tyres and seeing to that.

We discovered later that a smith would have charged us two pounds for fitting the drawbar. In the back of the car George had flung two tyres, entire strangers to us.

'One of them's new,' George said as we got ready to depart. 'Thirty shillings for the couple. An absolute gift at that. Men, horses, and cars is best well shod.'

Chapter Two

WE QUICK FURNISH

We now owned a car, a caravan on which we were £15 in debt, and Ian's adored motor-bike. Prudence urged us to dispose of this last since it could only be a hindrance and an expense, but we had a sentimental regard for the Matchless which had carried us both through blizzards and storms, so we hung on to the bike and proved caution wrong in this as in many other things. For the next fortnight we lived on the wind till my salary arrived.

We had many unhappy moments when we considered our *dishes* project. Even *our* optimism could not quite wave aside the many hindrances to success. There was, for instance, the difficulty of safe transport, there was the difficulty of choosing a wise and marketable stock, there was no one to whom we could turn for advice for the china merchants persisted in regarding us as a joke. Added to this there was the ominously pitying attitude of all our friends. Behind our backs they argued as to which of us had spoiled the other's career, while to our faces they refused to discuss our future as if by ignoring it they made it less disastrous.

The first Sunday in June was torrid, and on a hot day Aberdeen is the most infernal town with all her granite glittering and reflecting back the sun's radiance. We were so parched we felt we couldn't bear the town, and set out to leave it. On our way into the country we stopped and bought oranges in a crowded shop. 'Fruit!' we exclaimed together to the bewilderment of all the other customers.

No sooner had we decided on this other merchandise than all our difficulties resolved themselves magically, and we set to work once more on our altered plans. The more we thought of fruit the more persuaded we were of our wisdom in abandoning the dishes. Ian knew from bitter experience of the Highlands that fruit was very dear there in summer as well as winter, and he felt that there must be a large market amongst the throngs of summer visitors. The crowning touch to our relief came when we read in a newspaper of a fruit hawker who had failed to pay his income tax.

Our minds were at rest now, and there remained only the task of waiting the slow weeks till we were free.

By the middle of June we decided to find a camping-place for the caravan somewhere outside Aberdeen where Ian could live within reach of the University and where I could come on week-ends. Many reasons urged us towards this first camping, and not the least was that we could save our lodgings-money.

The Chalmers was still unlicensed, so we required some one to tow us to the chosen place which Ian had discovered on a hill overlooking the Dee. It was on a farm called Heldon Tree, where three brothers kept a dairy and hens, and they were pleased to let us set our van in a corner of their barn-yard. With the camping-place discovered, Ian went back to George White, who informed him casually that the day after we bought the caravan he was offered £70 for her by a man who was desperate for a dwelling-place. George agreed to flit us on Saturday, the 14th June, and his mother made the van clean for us.

All of a sudden Ian realized that he couldn't accompany George on the Saturday because he had a degree exam. to invigilate in the forenoon, so he sketched out the route for me since I must lead the redoubtable George to Heldon Tree.

I had now my salary, and on Friday the thirteenth —we seemed always to be hitting unlucky days, dates, and months—we began to spend it, starting with the Co-op. because we knew a member and could recover the divvy through her; we spent £4, 10s. on a hair mattress, pillows, and towels. Then we rushed to Woolworth's, where we spent a pound on knives, forks, dishes, casseroles and such like. I had often longed to spend a pound in Woolworth's, but it did not make so big a bundle after all. Pots and pans cost us 8s., and as an after-thought we paid 3s. 6d. for a frying-pan, which Ian

ultimately used to hold paraffin for cleaning the
Matchless; that was 3s. 6d. to the bad. We also
bought two kettles, a tin one to make tea over
picnic-fires and an enamel one for the stove. Just
then Ian stole guiltily away, and when I met him
again at the street corner I found he'd been buying
a .410 gun and a metal fishing-rod, which, complete
with line, hooks, reels, and cartridges, added a
further £2 to our bills. He pointed out with an air
of guilty pride that the .410 cost only twenty-five
bob. In the light of experience I think it was
twenty-five bob too much.

Next day I came down early to the caravan to
find George White's father, a fresh-faced old man
with blue eyes and a clerical hat, all ready to give
me coals and good advice about caravans and life
in general. When his son came he wished me luck;
for one was young only once, he said. It was the
first good-luck wished us.

At midday George towed our home to Heldon
Tree. He and I had a wild time until we got the
van set in its appointed place. George, in the midst
of endearments cried promiscuously to the cows, the
servant girl at the farm who came down to look on,
and the van, swore we'd got it in but by God we'd
never come out.

'I'll come and see to it, though,' he added.

Ian's invigilation was over and we had tea beside
the mill-wheel. Hens came pecking and clucking
under our noses, the sun shone, the water dripped,

we scrabbled our feet in the grass and were content.

Quite by chance our next new problem was solved as easily as the others had been. We had a home, we had a car, but how were we to carry and display our fruit, we wondered. Ian met a man in a garage who knew another man who had a light luggage-trailer to sell. There is something uncanny in the way men in garages always know other men who have something to sell. Anyway, Ian ran to inspect the trailer and we bought it for £2, 10s. The salary was melting fast. On the 30th of June we paid £6, 17s. 6d. for a quarter's licence for the Chalmers. Poor dear, her licence book revealed a mottled career. She'd been hackneyed from Land's End to Lochaber, trade car and private car by rapid turns.

Our jobs were done, we were free to go, but we lingered a few days at Heldon Tree making friends with the farming brothers and lying in the sun and getting to know all about Corybante and the caravan. The van was a bargain; it was roomy, twelve feet long and six feet wide, with plenty of cupboards and lockers and a good little Doctress stove and even a wardrobe. It had two bunks, to sleep four, but we stowed all our worldly goods, including one of the earliest Remington type-writers, Ian's pet pride (because no one else could work it), in the bottom bunk. (When he exchanged that old typewriter against a new one many years later he was given a little extra as antiquity value.)

And as for our van's appearance, that was quite handsome if one excepts the chimney, which inclined to lean drunkenly, now to one side, now to the other. But the van itself was painted dark blue outside with yellow piping round its panels, and inside the lining of three-ply panels was clear-varnished. There was inlaid linoleum on the floor, and the whole edifice was carried on the springs, wheels, and front axle of a pre-war Delaunay Belleville limousine.

At last, on an afternoon in early July, some friends came to have tea with us and we sat talking right into the summer evening. All at once we decided that this was our opportunity to get help to pack and go. That was no easy matter, for we had a car, a trailer, a caravan, a motor-bike, the old typewriter, which was about the size of a grand piano with as many keys, a suit-case or so full of books; clothes, papers; and pots and pans and dishes, and a hundred odds and ends forbye. Ian wanted to hitch the trailer on behind the caravan and so proceed to Speyside as if he were driving a train, but I rebelled because I'd have had to sit in the trailer all the way to keep a look-out behind. It's the law.

We began by cramming all our smaller belongings into the cupboards and lockers and into the bottom bunk of the van. Then we hitched the van to the car, no easy task. It took all our own and our friends' strength and the farmers' as well to turn the caravan round about and get it hooked to

George White's drawbar. When that was fixed we took the wheels and springs off the trailer and stuck them into Corybante's vast back-seat; the flat body of the trailer we hoisted and shoved into the caravan; it was only seven feet long and four feet wide so we managed that and wedged it against the stove. We thought now that we should try to get the van out of the hole in which she was sitting. There was a right-angled corner, too sharp to bring her round, between the stack-yard where we lay and the steep hill which climbed up towards the farm-house and the public road. In fact there was only one way to get her out, and that was over the found of a stack, a heap of large boulders which might easily capsize her. Ian chanced it and gave Corybante her head. The rest of us stood back sweating and shouting 'She'll never do it'. For a ghastly moment the lurching van poised on one wheel, but she righted herself and in a moment she was on the highway. We halted there.

It had been our intention to sleep till dawn and set out then; there was something intoxicating in seeing everything so nearly ready for the journey; we decided not to wait another moment. The van was opened and many hands made lightish work of lifting the three-hundredweight Matchless into the van. Ian took off her handlebars to let her front wheel enter the narrow door, and without further ceremony the lower half of the door was shut on her; Ian climbed in by the top half of the door and jammed everything that threatened to move with the trestles for holding up the caravan when she was not on the road. So at ten o'clock on a warm summer evening we moved gently down the hill towards Aberdeen. We were off.

Chapter Three

WE FLY BY NIGHT

We went anxiously down the hill from Heldon Tree, and waving a wild farewell to the mill-wheel and our friends, we entered Aberdeen through one of these embattled crowds of small boys who seemed to spring from the pavements wherever we went. The inexpertly balanced caravan rocked; Corybante shook her hind wheels in the air like a skittish cow; I kept one hand on the car door and one eye on the caravan behind us; Ian preferred to look straight ahead, on the principle I suppose that what the eye does not see cannot grieve the heart. The trailer wheels slid forward until they found a comfortable resting-place in the small of my back.

The Chalmers bellowed into the still evening. The long climb out of the city over Tirebagger Hill set the radiator boiling, and midges made frantic spirals round the column of steam while we prayed heartily that the long drought had not dried up all the roadside streams.

It was the bonniest evening. Dusk rose like a mist towards the lighted sky, cows went to fields of clover from their milking, and lights broke here and there in cottage windows. All of a sudden we

became happy and free from care. We sang and
the Chalmers shouted, and colts in the fields galloped
to look at us and followed us until they came bang
up against fences, over which they leaned with
prick ears and long, silly, astonished faces.

When we crossed Tirebagger it was eleven
o'clock and our petrol tank was nearly empty. We
had counted on garages by the way, but village after
village was dark and already sunk in sleep, with not
a garage open, and we began to wonder with some
anxiety if we could get petrol before our tank ran
dry. We had more than a hundred miles before us
this night. We were afraid to camp by the roadside
for our car had battery ignition; if we ran our
battery down burning lights all night we were
stranded before we had well begun. We rocked on
towards Inverurie, where garage after garage had
closed doors. We began to question passers-by
desperately whether there was a night-garage in
the town. At last we found a petrol-station where
the boss was making up his books. He sold us ten
gallons of commercial petrol. We reckoned that
this saving of 1s. 8d. because we bought commercial
petrol was as good as money earned. Is not a penny
saved a penny earned?

Seven or eight men and the inevitable mob of
small boys gathered to look at us, and as the tank
was filled we took a moment's leisure to look likewise at ourselves. We were filthy dirty from all our
labours in the farm-yard. But our dirty dishevelled

'Hey, tinkies!'

appearance was trig and neat compared with the
appearance of our equipage. Corybante it is true
retained, perhaps by mere dint of size, some shreds
of dignity even with commercial petrol in her guts.
She was always herself. But behind her the
caravan yawed. Its windows had jolted open, its
curtains flapped feebly in the night air, its chimney
sat askew, and one of its tyres was flat. The trailer
wheels had at last come to rest; one wheel was deep
in the back of the car, the other stood high in the
air over the side of the car, and our bed-quilt, which
we carried in the car in case the night turned very
cold, was wrapped round the axle and the wheel.
We looked rather as if we were Huns returning
with their booty after a raid on a city's washing-
lines. And all the little boys called to each other,
down the street and up the street, '*Hey, tinkies!*'

The garage man demanded in a conspiratorial
whisper where was our rear light? He went
further and said if we were nabbed now for having
no rear light, where were the brakes on caravan
wheels controlled from car? Ian was suddenly
inspired; he broke somehow into the caravan,
being heaved in at the upper half of the door by
some of the sightseers. Dishes inside fell with an
appalling clatter, and a little boy was rude enough
to advise every one exactly what dish that was. Ian
took the rear lamp from the motor-bike and we
screwed it to the back of the van and tied the
generator with string to the handle of the van door.

'Our road dived and twisted and climbed.'

The rubber tube from the generator to the rear light was slit, but Ian's hankie fixed that. The red light shone!

A little dog epitomized the attitude of Inverurie by lifting his leg against the wheel of the caravan. We departed with minds less happy than they had been. Why had every one laughed? Why did no one take us seriously? But we actually succeeded in overtaking and passing a car, and that restored our self-respect. Huntly went by in hollow reverberating tones. It was a most magnificent and lovely night.

The smell of clover beat like wings about us and our road dived and twisted and climbed, always climbed, into the dark hills which girded the northern horizon. The burns were dry from long drought. Then at last we came to the high ridge beneath which lay Morayshire and the sea. The smell of the sea came to us as fresh as morning light and still the long dark road swept down, flowing like a river through the lovely woods of Fochabers.

We crossed the Spey, along whose course our road would go so many times before winter came on us near the river's frozen source; we looked solemnly down to the swift stream, for crossing it we entered a new region; the old world of our lives was left behind. The Spey was our Rubicon.

Nothing moved on the earth except the road and the wind before dawn, and the proud tops of the

fir-trees waiting for dawn and the sun their lord.
Towards Elgin two men stranded by the roadside
asked for oil, but we had none; they lighted a tiny
fire. Beyond Elgin we saw a huge bonfire shower
sparks to the kindred flame in the sky. It was long
past midnight, after two o'clock. In a moment we
were passing the field where the bonfire blazed only
a few yards from the roadside. A crowd of figures
bolted from beside the fire to look at us, lads and
boys shouting and singing and waving bare black
arms. Their young voices followed us a long way,
and we remembered them and spoke of them,
wondering what brought them there, until we were
past Rothes, where we began to see a heavy pall
of smoke on the horizon in front of us. There was
never such a night of fire. The smoke came from
a farm-steading close to the right-hand side of the
road; the roof was blazing with a great noise of
fire and falling timbers. We got out as quickly as
we could, wondering whether the farm folk had
discovered the fire or no. As we ran towards the
flaming steading we cannoned into a distraught man
who was herding cattle from the byre and shouting
orders and questions to no one in particular. Pigs
ran skirling about his feet, in their frenzy making
for the fire from which they were being rescued.
We snatched hold of a white-headed youth to bawl
in his ear 'Can we help?' He snorted and galloped
away to drag some trifling pieces of harness from the
stable. Ian caught him by the braces and roared in

his ear, 'Is there a telephone or fire-brigade near?'
But we could get no coherent reply.

By this time the fire was almost all flame, and as
the smoke grew less, day came over the hills to see
this rival conflagration. We decided to go to Aber-
lour for the police, but when we tried to reverse
Corybante we stuck broadside across the road.   It
was our first discovery of a fact we were to strike
our heads against several times; you can't reverse
a car with a heavy trailer.

We ended by knocking up the postmaster of a
near-by village.   That official came out clad in
heavy flannel pants, his shirt, and a night-cap, to
snarl at us and send phone-calls. We roused all the
houses in the neighbourhood and men came with
buckets from all sides, but there was no water, the
drought had dried it up.   There was some talk of
cutting the roof, and men on ladders made a great
show of gallantry with axes and pick-axes until
their women-folk dragged them down and scolded
them. We could do no more than stand and watch
the bonny wicked thing while it played itself
destroying the labours and the hopes of men.

We could do no good there, so wearily now we
wrenched the caravan straight and made towards
Grantown.   Rabbits crossed the road in herds and
droves until Ian brought out the .410, when there
was not a rabbit visible for miles. We halted for
a moment beside a grassy clearing near Cromdale.
Rabbits began to troop from a field of corn.   One

sat up to look at us, and Ian shot it at the third attempt. It was an old tough buck but welcome nevertheless, as a token no less than as a meal.

We could not get to Grantown because the bridge over the Spey was closed, so we kept along the east side of the river in the direction of Nethy Bridge. We halted beside a little attenuated stream to wash ourselves and make tea. I fried eggs and bread; Ian made tinker's tea; drummy tea he calls it, because the tramps and navvies who make it most use an old tin-can with a wire-handle to boil it in, their *drummy*. You pour water and milk into the drummy, float a handful of tea gently on the surface, and boil as quickly as possible, taking care not to shake the drum and to keep the leaves floating on the surface until the water boils. There's no tea so good.

We were refreshed but still tired, and we could not halt until we found a camping-place to take the van off the road. While the kettle boiled to wash us we lifted the motor-bike from the caravan. It weighed three hundredweights normally but now it seemed to weigh a ton. Oil had run out of its tank on to the floor; there were ashes from the stove everywhere. Ian hunted for a camping-place and left me to guard the van and contemplate the mess. He found one soon, but when we reached it, it took us two hours to get the van on its trestles and fit to sleep in. Ian wanted to make a bed in the awful mess and wait for another time to tidy

C

up, but I couldn't do that. We built a fire of fir roots to boil water and I scrubbed out the van and tidied up the papers and the typewriter and the oil-stains and the muck of ashes, while Ian dammed a little well to make a drinking-place. We slept like the dead until late afternoon, squatters and refugees and very tired.

CULREOCH

CULREOCH

of bog-myrtle and fir-resin filled
the country. When a thunderstorm came we sat
in the caravan listening to lightning crack with a
noise like a whip between us and the fir-trees. It
was lovely and terrifying, but still no rain fell.

Chapter Four

WE LIE LOW

Culreoch, our new camping-place, was very well
suited to be our first base for fruit-hawking.
Villages were dotted all around us, parched multitudes of summer visitors filled the country. But
we were scarcely ready to begin to sell fruit. We
were tired and jaded and headachy. And this
break with all we knew was too serious to be made
in a furious hurry while we were tired. So we
sat quiet for a few days while the sun-baked
country took on autumn colours before summer
was well begun.

We fell straight into love with Culreoch. On
the other side of the belt of trees in which we
camped, the moor reached straight to the Cairngorms. The smell of bog-myrtle and fir-resin filled
the country. When a thunderstorm came we sat
in the caravan listening to lightning crack with a
noise like a whip between us and the fir-trees. It
was lovely and terrifying, but still no rain fell.

While we rested the country was alive and busy
all around. Sheep came to look at us, and ate
our potato peelings. We watched them being
dipped in the sheepfold which was only a couple

of hundred yards away from the van. We helped
to boil the water for their dip, stoking a huge
boiler with resiny roots. Dogs yapped, lambs cried
for their mothers, the shepherds plunged sheep
after sheep into the bath; all day the sun blazed
and in the evening we bathed in a quiet pool in
the Spey.

A few days lounging soon drove all the city
weariness from our bones and heads and we began
to make our final plans. We took the motor-bike
to Grantown and must have looked like a pair of
caterans when we descended on that gentle town-
ship. Ian looked more like a gangster than even
Nature intended, for he surveyed the world from a
pair of grim eyes well ringed with grit. He was
nattily attired in knee-boots and a tattered Storm-
guard coat. As pillion passenger, and small at that,
I wasn't nearly so conspicuous in my breeches and,
of all things, a French-model hat. When we came
into the main street of Grantown we found the
whole place waving and cheering in front of us.
I thought it very charming of Grantown to welcome us like this and yelled in Ian's ear that I
wished we had taken Corybante instead of the
Matchless. But my spouse had come all over self-
conscious, and setting his teeth in a peculiarly
vicious fashion he wrenched the bike round a
corner and bolted down a side street. To my
expostulations he said that if we'd remained in the
High Street the outraged inhabitants would have

lynched us for spoiling the look of the place. So
we hid the Matchless outside the bounds of Grantown and returned by devious streets to view the
festivities. We arrived just in time to see a grand
procession go by. Red Indians on plough horses,
Boadicea on a milk-cart, town big-wigs on their
dignity, girl guides on their best behaviour—all
went trooping along the street under a banner
which reached across the thoroughfare and read

CEUD MILLE FAILTE

Ian asked one of the onlookers what it meant,
and he said 'I prefer a Bass', but actually I think
it is a Gaelic welcome.

There were to be speeches later but we did not
wait for them; instead, we hunted for fruiterers'
shops to find if they were prosperous, and if they
were dear. They were both, and the discovery
lightened our hearts. If these people could prosper
on the prices they charged, there was room for us.

But our joy in this discovery was lessened when
we found that all prices, not fruit prices alone,
were at least a third more than they were in
Aberdeen. We grudged 2s. 4d. a pound for
toughish steak.

Next day we made a grand tour through all the
country round. Every village was crammed with
tourists, and everywhere fruit was dear.

We sorely disliked paying high prices for everything we bought, but I am not sure whether the

expense of living in Speyside was not a good thing
—though well disguised. It taught us to make
the most of our money by spending carefully and
wisely. I think it also helped me to cook better
because I couldn't afford costly things and I had
to make tasty nourishing dishes out of cheap in-
gredients. Woolworth's casseroles were a blessing
when it came to eking out tough beef with plenty
of potatoes and onions. I am sure that poverty
like necessity is the mother of inventiveness in
cookery at least. A bare cupboard makes the best
stew.

We had to take care of our money because we
had not so much of it and there were heavy ex-
penses ahead. We had to buy our first consignment of fruit out of our capital; to put sides on
the trailer; there was always petrol to pay for;
we hadn't bought our hawker's licence yet (we
never did!).

We cut down every possible expense. In Aberdeen we bought coals for the van stove by the stone,
in the poorest quarter of the town, paying fourpence the stone for it, which wasn't really economy
but saved cartage and mess in the caravan. We
wanted to buy a hundredweight of coal in Grantown, but the merchants were very sniffy about
such a trifling quantity, and somehow we grudged
buying dear coal more than anything else, perhaps
because we thought it a shame that the laborious
job of mining the coal should only account for about

a quarter of the total cost. Ian suddenly recalled that people had been fined for gathering coals along the side of railway lines during a coal strike. So we rose early one Sabbath morning and went down to the main Speyside line which ran along the valley about half a mile from our van. We collected a sackful of coal before the cocks crowed.

We were soon very expert about the business and committed our larceny like old hands. We came to know the bends in the line where the rails were banked and the wagons rocked, toppling lumps of coal over their sides. It was funny to find ourselves grumbling because it was steam coal and didn't catch easily.

We were so pleased with ourselves that we resolved to live even further off the country. I was all for real scrounging, but Ian pointed out coldly that we were hawkers, not reivers. He went further to say that I was simply reverting to the type of my Lochaber ancestors.

Late one Saturday evening I discovered that we had no food for the next day and the shops were shut. Ian smiled in a superior way and said we'd get food all right. We took the motor-bike and fishing-tackle and went into the hills near Tomintoul. A bitter wind rose, which was more than the trout did. Ian was reduced at last to guddling for tiny little trout under stones with his hands, and by the time it was dark we had a dozen. We fried them as soon as we got back to the van. That expedition was really a dead loss because it made us so hungry that we ate far more food then we caught.

Ian's poaching ancestors were strong enough in him to keep him awake till dawn imagining who knows what forays and great deer. He woke me with the first light of day to give me bitterly strong coffee. We took the Matchless and the .410 past Nethy Bridge and upwards along the Nethy into Tulloch, into a wilderness of ravines and rocks and meandering roads and scarred blackened tree-trunks which were burnt when the forest of Rothiemurchus went on fire about fifteen years ago. We saw a steam-roller in the very heart of that dreich place lying like the soul of desolation in a gravel pit, a melancholy neglected thing; but we never saw a rabbit.

We bumped and bucketed further into the hills until the Cairngorms reared their grand steeps over us, but we saw scarcely a living creature. It was not till long afterwards that we discovered that the winters in Tulloch are so wild that all small creatures leave the place or die and so the moors are without rabbits and the morning noise of birds.

The sun rose and our road made a circle to bring us back to the Spey. There were rabbits in plenty, but all of them close to houses. The sun climbed and I began to think it was time we were home, for country people rise betimes, but Ian kept on blazing away volleys from the .410 without hitting a rabbit.

'We collected a sackful of coal.'

A roe-buck gazed pensively at us from a field of
hay. He was too bonny to shoot at and he was a
poacher like ourselves. We passed the caravan;
rooks cawed and the gun banged and rabbits sat on
their heels to look at us, and to this day I can't
understand why he did not rouse the whole country.
A little dell beside the road was moving with rabbits.
Ian prepared to stalk a fat old buck who was sunning
himself in front of his burrow. I watched while
Ian spent some time crawling about, and just as he
was getting a bead on the creature I cried *Woa*!
I had just seen an old man who lay sleeping in the
dust of the roadside twenty yards further along
from where we had laid down the motor-bike. His
venerable head was laid on his jacket, his old body
was covered with two potato bags, his toes looked
through his boots, and a pram full of strange odds
and ends rested beside him. We left him to his
slumber and carried on, desperately determined and
almost without hope of ever getting a rabbit. Then
our petrol ran dry and Ian hid the .410 down his
trouser leg and we pushed the motor-bike home
past honest decent folk in Sunday clothes who
looked askance at us for the tramps we were. We
were glad to get home to sleep; I made a sort of a
dinner with macaroni and scraps and we were glad
to buy meat even at 2s. 4d. the pound for some
time to come.

Chapter Five

WE BECOME NEWS-CORRESPONDENTS

When we decided to sell dishes as a means of liveli-
hood we supposed that the more country we
covered the better. Many things contributed to
modify our first grandiose scheme. When we
exchanged dishes for fruit we realized that we must
have a base where we could collect supplies regularly. We could have carried a stock of dishes, but
fruit meant daily fresh supplies, and that tied us to
a limited area and a fixed centre.

Of course, when we visualized ourselves covering
the whole North of Scotland we hadn't reckoned on
the train of vehicles we now possessed. If we'd
succeeded in getting the motor-bus we hunted for
it would have been house, store, shop, and vehicle,
all in one. But as things were, we couldn't move
from one place to another without spending hours
in packing and unpacking our possessions, loading
and unloading the motor-bike and trailer into the
van, hoisting the caravan off its trestles and jacking
it up again to get it back on its trestles, and man-
handling it until it could be attached to the car.
We reconciled ourselves to the modest idea of
having a base, but the question arose where the

base should be. It was answered in a rather extraordinary way.

In an expansive moment Ian had written a circular letter to all the newspapers he could think of offering himself as a news-correspondent. He carefully concealed everything except the fact that he travelled a great deal through the Highlands— and that was more of a prophecy than a fact; he added that he heard all the news worth hearing and that the editors might do worse than appoint him as their representative. He did not say that he was an embryonic hawker married to a vagabond, but by a skilful mixture of prophecy, inaccuracy, over-statement and understatement he was fortunate enough to impress a number of highly respectable and dignified journals. It was not long till we discovered that the imposing inaccuracies of his statements, and his cheek, were the virtues of news-correspondents.

The most dignified of all the newspapers told us that it had no representative in the village of Newtonmore and that it required a daily weather report from that place. We considered seriously. Newtonmore had advantages as a base, and not least was the shilling a day we'd get for the weather report; it would do more than keep Ian in tobacco. And Newtonmore was a village crowded with visitors; there were excellent roads radiating from it into a country rich in tourists but poor in fruit. Yes, Newtonmore had advantages, but in an imperfect world it was not without its drawbacks. The chief of these was the presence there of hordes of the Macpherson clan all closely and angrily related to Ian. I shrank from encountering thousands of disapproving and loquacious relatives, but hardly dared mention this in the face of Ian's royal contempt for village opinion. In any case, as he pointed out, we didn't need to live in Newtonmore to see the weather there.

At this time we were unsatisfactory correspondents, for our news sense had yet to develop into what it became later when everything, fire, flood, life, and the fear of death, became food for it. Nevertheless we felt that we must do something to justify our name and establish ourselves in the good graces of our editors as well as to make a little money out of our neighbours' affairs. So we took the Matchless one brilliant afternoon and departed westward up Speyside to the high village of Dalwhinnie. There we met several people with whom Ian had been friendly since his student days, when he spent his summers ghillieing and navvying in that direction. He hunted up a youth who had blossomed into a gamekeeper since Ian last saw him. George was full of news about deer-forests and grouse-moors. We reckoned that news from moors and forests was bound to be of interest at this time, so soon before the 12th of August. As if to the manner born, Ian produced pencil and note-book.

It was a sad story we heard. George assured us

that there had never been such a year since forests were first made. I had not realized until then what poverty an unlet moor or deer-forest meant to the surrounding countryside. George named one unlet forest after another as Ian scribbled the famous names; estates untenanted for the first time in their history. We tried to make a rough reckoning of the huge total loss to the country in wages, rents, and trade.

Rain came pelting before we had gone far towards Kingussie, where Ian made his first and last interview, with a retired schoolmaster, who quizzed Ian more than Ian questioned him; Ian met me in a very nervous state when it was all over, and I could see him avoiding people in Kingussie for many a long day afterwards in case they saw him and said, 'Oh, there's that fellow Cameron from Glasgow who interviewed So and So.' I think he gave a fake name, address, and everything else to the inquisitive teacher.

Ian has tried to justify himself with, 'I was interviewing him for a purpose, I explained, and he gave me the right to question him by granting the interview; but it was sheer damned curiosity which made him catechize me, and it's easier to tell a tale than be rude.'

Two days later we were astounded to see the forest and grouse-moor news which we had sent billed on placards throughout Grantown, flaunting in huge red letters outside newsagents' shops. We were rather appalled by what we had done, and slunk out of town with the feeling that every one knew it was we who had been washing the dirty linen of the Highlands in public.   A mile from the town we began to feel better and count our hypothetical gains;   and it *was* nice that our first attempt at news-corresponding should be a success.   The pennies it brought would make it easier to carry on in the early days of our fruit-hawking.

Encouraged by the effort, Ian wrote to a very dignified newspaper asking whether a shilling was the maximum for fishing reports. The editor wrote back pointing out that there was no need to trouble ourselves or him with news of parochial affairs or such trifles (and he listed them) as Girl Guide camps, Bands of Hope, Church Sales of Work. He went on to say that he wanted and would pay well for exclusive news of national importance such as murder stories, news of railway or road disasters; but it was left for yet another newspaper to wish us a good New Year and a nice hill-climbing tragedy.

D

Chapter Six

WE ARE WEIGHED AND FOUND WANTING

We knew nothing about fruit except its retail price, but what was more important, we knew nothing of business and scarcely how to think of starting to search for fruit-merchants, or their places of business. However, the newspapers which we bought in bundles to see what they had made of our moor and forest story disclosed that there had been a new departure in the fruit-importing business. London, we gathered, used to be the only importing and distributing centre in Britain, but now fruit-ships had begun to unload Scotland's quota direct in Glasgow. We decided to go to Glasgow, and asked the advice of a friend living there. He bade us come down.

It was now Friday the eleventh of July, and we were most anxious to begin business as soon as ever we could; time simply flew past; it was there, and in a moment the days and weeks were gone and summer grew old even as we watched it flower.

We garaged Corybante in the steading of the farm where we bought our milk. We had sunshine for thirty miles on our way until we crossed Drum-

ochter Pass, and there rain from the west met us.
Far beneath us in wooded Perthshire sullen clouds
loomed across our path, and we began to be afraid
that the weather was going to break just at the
moment when we needed it most, for our journey,
and for our trade.

This journey at least disappointed our fears. We
seemed to ride between rain-storms, with roads wet
all the way, clouds behind us and before, but above
us the sky was blue. We took it for a prosperous
omen as we dropped like a plummet for falling
miles from the bleak border country of Perth and
Inverness, down to Blair Atholl, to Pitlochry, with
only the occasional buffeting of a stray wind, and
the sight of wet roads, and a drop or two of rain
from the skirts of a cloud, to keep us in mind of the
weather.

We felt almost as if we had changed our country
and our climate when we left Inverness behind.
Instead of the gaunt hills we knew, instead of bleak
moors and stone-bespreckled hill-sides, we had on
either hand hills wooded to their summit with the
generous green of beech and ash and oak. The
sombre firs which mostly clothe Speyside were here
replaced by hardwoods; even the Garry, for all its
falls and foaming over rocks, had a gentle air which
the streams of Speyside seldom show. We were in
a strange and to us exotic place; the narrowness
of the valley through Killiecrankie and down to
Pitlochry increased the air of sheltered warmth the

country wore; we had grown accustomed to the
wide valley of the Spey and great hills far off.

As we passed through Killiecrankie the loveliness
of the country was warm and soft in our eyes and
mouths, almost as if we breathed and tasted it. The
rain-washed trees and houses overhung with trees,
the soft sweet air, were like the waters of a
warm sea to wanderers from a harsh dry country
far off.

We passed houses set beneath the steep wooded
hills so beautifully that when they passed we were
not sure if we had come by them, or if they were
part in a dream; their bright roofs, their gardens,
the climbing-flowers upon their walls, were the
clear pebbles and the bright sea-weed which
adorned the bottom of this green-sea world.

It was the age of our innocence. When we pass
that way now, it is in haste to retreat again to
Speyside, to the bare moors and circling hills; and
when we see houses that are picturesque, we
wonder what they are like inside, and how the
people live, and what they do, and do they drink
black boiled tea; what sanitation they have; is the
landlord as bad as most Highland landlords; do the
hills behind pour water into the houses.

But then we saw only that they set themselves
perfectly in a perfect setting. Vast aged trees
mocked their own years with their exuberant
foliage; trees climbed to the zenith, huge green
waves which had their crests higher than we could

turn our eyes to see. Only the pass through which
the Garry fell was dark, a sunless gorge far beneath
the limits of light, where Graham of Claverhouse
dying asked, 'Is it well for King James?' and being
told 'Yes', shut his eyes to murmur, 'Then it
matters the less for me', before he died with all his
sins upon him, and all the blood of many a bitter
fight.

The road went past us, and rivers flowed, and
named villages sped by like a tale of old adventures.
We had never come this way before, never bought
oranges in a roadside shoppie near Kenmore before,
thinking as we bought that our next purchase
would be in hundredweights instead of single
oranges; we had never till now resisted the Tay's
temptation to bathe, nor gathered wild strawberries
in Kenmore woods. We wound along the quiet
shores of Loch Tay, and thence by Balquhidder and
Strathyre and many another storied place until our
minds were all a jumble of names and half-for-
gotten tales and winding climbing roads.

We entered Glasgow and found our friend with
the help of many Highland and Irish-voiced policemen, and of stray people besides those official
guides; we had never been in Glasgow before,
where one is not only directed, but actually led,
towards the place one wants to find, by utter
strangers who disregard their own business for
minutes at a time in order to put one on one's way.
It was not like Aberdeen, this immediate friendli-

ness and helpfulness; it was not like any other town we knew.

We spent Saturday forenoon in the Fruit Market; but the deals seemed all to be in thousands of cases and the bidding was conducted with such cryptic remarks and obscure gestures that we despaired of ever getting our small bids in; and we were really afraid that we might nod at the wrong time or in the wrong way and find ourselves landed with a cargo of several thousands of cases of fruit. We had another special pencil and a note-book, and with these we quitted the uproarious centre of the fruit trade in order to make a round of the stalls. But though we produced our pencil and note-book with an air of great efficiency, the rapid-fire talk of the salesmen was so much gibberish to us. We were handed fruit to sample, and squeezed it, trying to look wise and hoping that a squeeze was the correct treatment for this particular type of fruit; we were handed small fruit to sample, and I think we did the wrong thing when we ate it instead of biting out a mouthful and spitting it away. The salesmen, sleek insolent young men, or smooth, courteous—oh, so patient—young men, or young men in a hurry, rattled out their piece something like this: '*Very nice sir newly arrived punnets trays crates and cases shall we say seven three the hundredweight in ton lots f.o.b. These sir a very special ten three the same——.*'

When we had made a great number of inconclusive calls and eaten a great many apples and plums we began to think that business for the day would end before we got anywhere, so at last we walked boldly into an office which seemed busy and whose fruit was nicely set out. We were seized and snatched away by a salesman who hurled us into lifts, flung us down to chilly, humid chambers where bananas hung in myriads, whirled us up to giddy heights where apples lay dry and cool, down again to the ground floor to inspect the day's consignment of Californian fruits. All the sweets of the world were piled before us, and I think if Satan had shown the fruits instead of the riches of the world the Temptation would have been more terrible. The air was laden with the smell of fruit, but we concealed our wonder and pleasure as best we could while we ordered a bushel case of apples, a crate of Canary bananas, a 12 lb. basket of Scotch tomatoes, a 12 lb. tray of Californian plums, a case of South African oranges and a case of grapefruit.

It was a solemn business, this our first purchase of fruit, and it was made the more difficult because we had to find out how many oranges and apples went to a case, how many grapefruit; we had to make up our minds what fruit to buy and what particular sort of apples and oranges to invest in, without knowing the first thing about the business, and without letting the salesman guess our ignorance, because we did not trust even dealers in the finest-smelling fruits to refrain from taking a little advantage of ignorance. We were assured that our case of oranges would contain no less than three hundred, sound fruit all ; that the grapefruit would number eighty and the apples weigh forty odd pounds; and the whole consignment would be forwarded to Kingussie station without fail on Monday the 21st July, in time to arrive there on Tuesday morning. Our common sense should have told us not to ask fruit to be despatched on a long journey on a Monday. But it did not; we were being clever about so many things we had no time to use our common sense.

We paid four pounds and sixteen shillings for our order, and though it was a lot of money we seemed to have bought a great deal for it; besides, the oranges were so golden, the apples smelled so fine, we felt, like Omar, that the merchants had lost on the bargain.

Then it was Glasgow's week-end. We began by liking the city's hurly-burly; its higgledy-piggledy streets where costly fur-shops lie cheek by jowl with cheap butchers; where women in rich furs mingle in the same shops with their poorer sisters from down-town (if this most democratic city really has up-town or down-town) in shawls. We gazed with awe at the lavish profusion of Glasgow's food and tobacco and spirit shops; here are no huge windows empty and bare in the approved modern fashion of window-dressing; but the tobacconists spill whole hundredweights of every conceivable tobacco into their windows and let the passers-by gaze at a shop that is like a smoker's Arabian Night's dream of tobacco; the vintners roll kegs and casks of whisky and sherry and port into their windows and flank them with scores upon scores of bottles heaped higgledy-piggledy as if the owner of the shop disdained the meagre habits of men who arrange bottles in ranks and rows; butchers hang immense carcases of cattle and sheep and pigs in their great windows, and every grocer and every baker piles as much food into the windows as would feed the city for weeks. We had never seen anything so lavish in our lives; we had never seen the most abject poverty so strangely confused in street and shop with evident wealth. Here was a city which loved good food and plenty of it; loved tobacco and sweet cream-cakes and port from the wood and whisky from the cask; which disdained to be nice and pernickety about its food or drink, and lived in a glorious kindly confusion, sooty and fog-stained indeed, but so lavish it was never drab.

Sunday in Glasgow was Sunday in Glasgow; we admired the miraculous deformity of Glasgow University, set on its hill-top like the soul of modern slummed cities looking away towards the modern clippit promised land of Corporation Housing Schemes and Deferred Payment Bungalows where rich and poor are at last segregated; in whose streets shawls do not jostle furs; where shops are nice and

refined and no longer glorious with excess of everything they sell.

But we were country people; the city though it
pleased us was not for us; it made us prisoners,
walled in by crowds and dirty fog-laden air and the
rows and rows of houses filled with terrifying
multitudes of people. We began to worry about
our fruit, and about the dark future when we should
sell no fruit and what would become of us then,
poor things. We waited for Monday to let us finish
our shopping. We must go on buying what we
were sure no one would buy.

We had weights and scales to get. We found the
names of several firms who sold weighing-machines,
and whilst I did some small shopping for food Ian
went to find out about the scales. The shop he
came to first was an enormous place filled with
cash-registers and great grave owl-faced weighing-
machines. But before he could escape a salesman
pounced on him with a 'Yes, *Sir*?' A clockwork
contrivance snecked the door behind him and there
he was, trapped in that ghoulish dim hall of the
soulless and wonderful machine.

'Yes, *Sir*,' said the salesman, 'what can I interest
you in?' and without halting for an answer he
almost sold Ian a cash-register. When Ian would
have none of that he was led by easy stages past
scales which could weigh a hair, past machines
which rejected bad coins until at last in the inner-
most Holy of Holies he was brought face to face

with the latest and most abominable invention. Is it not queer how a machine becomes more inhuman the better it imitates humanity's actions?

It could weigh, it counted, it kept accounts, it checked pilfering, it encouraged trade, it was like nothing so much as one of these Credit Schemes for curing trade-depression. What does it think of the gold standard? Ian is driven to asking. The salesman flushes to the roots of his hair and asks stiffly, 'What do you require?'

'A small scales for a van,' my husband replied.

He was shown a variety of huge machines.

'What do these things cost?' he demanded.

It appeared that costs were not this salesman's department. He summoned an underling, who whispered.

'Forty pounds—sixty pounds—a hundred pounds, Ian was told as the salesmen went from one machine to another.

Ian shook his head.

'You can have them on deferred purchase,' he was told. 'Ten pounds down, the rest in monthly payment——'

'Have you anything so common as an ordinary shop scales?' Ian interrupted.

'I'm sorry, sir. *We* are specialists.'

I met Ian at lunch-time and we taigled dispiritedly along a quiet street. Suddenly we espied a tiny shop and on it a placard saying, 'Sale. Weights and Scales.' We paid seven and sixpence

for what we wanted.   Our luck had changed, for on
the opposite side of the street we spied a paper-bag
manufacturer who sold us brown bags in two sizes
by weight.   There now remained only the tarpaulin
to cover our trailer and keep dust from our fruit
as we went on our rounds.   We sent an order to a
wholesale firm in Aberdeen in which we had a
friend.   The bill for the tarpaulin, as we discovered
later, was 13s. 4d.   All our preparations were made
at last and we could leave Glasgow; we could begin
to brave Speyside.

'What does it think of the gold standard?'

Chapter Seven

WE ENCAMP BESIDE ANOTHER BURN

We left Glasgow in a smirr of rain which made the streets greasy and the tram rails dangerous. We twice took wrong turnings, and until we came to greenish fields again on the road to Stirling we felt as if every turning was a wrong turning, and even when we reached the open country we felt tired and lack-lustre like people who have come through a long draggling illness. The roads were wet and the day gloomed, even the line of hills beyond Stirling scowled on the plain instead of inviting us. I bought Wellingtons in Stirling, and when we had paid for that and for two pies and a few apples to stay our hunger, our purse was empty except for as much money as would pay our petrol; I kept a little emergency store knotted in my handkerchief.

A mile north of Dunkeld the sun shone for a few moments. We halted to warm ourselves at its brief embers. We ate our pies, and had for dessert raspberries and wild strawberries that we found growing at the roadside.

A deluge of rain came on as we passed through Pitlochry, and lashed our faces as we scurried through Drumochter. The wind heeled the bike

over, the rain bruised our faces; and then all of a
sudden we were over the summit of Drumochter,
and in front of us the sun illumined the Monadhliaths. We were almost dry again when we came
to Nethy Bridge, but we were bone-weary and dirty
and tired. We left the bike at the iron bridge over
the Spey close to Nethy Bridge and went down to
the river to a pool overhung by alders. The river
talked peaceably of country things; its waters
cleaned us and rested us; the river said *Home
Again* over and over to us, and Glasgow's weariness
was washed away with the city's grime.

The evening light was limpid like the water of
the small Spey. The sun descended towards the
Monadhliaths, from whose high scarp evening walked
down to woods of birch and fir. Between the woods
and the riverside-fields a line of dog-roses marked
the course of the road to Grantown, and higher
towards the woods farm-houses looked at the shining
Cairngorms; miles of level moor stretched through
Tulloch towards the east and glowed in the light
of the sun. A great yellow scarf of whins went past
the houses, fringe of gold to the dark mantle of the
firs. All the east shone, there was not an unlighted
window in the great sweep of valley east of the
Spey, but all shone back to the sun and the dark
hills of the west.

We lay half drugged with content in a tiny dell
by the river. Round us were thickets of roses,
single bushes of wild roses, and a solitary yellow

garden rose brought by some chance to this place
to mock with its more lasting flowers the sudden
beauty and more sudden decay of the wild white
and red roses native here.

The place was full of noises: noise of bees; of the
river; distant lowing of cattle; voices in the dim
west. Evening came on with pleasant steps, down
to our herb-grown water-meadow, and at last the
sun was gone from sight, the Monadhliaths were
black against the sky, dew fell, making the meadows
rank with the smell of herbs and flowers, thyme and
mint and small lowly flowers which now rivalled
their upstart neighbours the roses which had so
long flaunted themselves before the sun. Crowfoot,
clover, vetches, all became as fine as any rose.

We turned at last to Culreoch; it was pleasant to
come home to our own abode and to drink cold
water from our own well which we made and
protected.

Holidays were at an end. We returned from
Glasgow on the 14th and on the 15th we uprooted
ourselves from Culreoch to find a camping-place
further west in Badenoch near Newtownmore. It
was afternoon before we had everything packed and
ready to remove; the Matchless had to be lifted into
the van, and we had no friends to help us this time;
we were glad once more that we had given up the
idea of constantly changing our quarters.

We drank farewell to Culreoch in the frosty
water of our little pool. Its bog-myrtle and resin-

'A tiny dell by the river.'

ous firs, its chill water and blazing sun, were all at
once something to remember, all at once they were
in the past. We halted on the iron bridge over the
Spey to look down upon the beflowered meadows.
A policeman asked us if we weighed three tons,
because the bridge was closed to heavy traffic.

We had to visit Newtonmore to send our weather
report. As we passed through Kingussie all the
people stared and Ian wondered why, though he
should have been accustomed to it by now. But I
told him that perhaps it was because as we went
through I took the pipe he had given me to hold
and began to pretend to smoke it, and when the
people looked I bowed to right and left—like
royalty, you know. He was not very pleased.

I think our procession was even more disreputable than usual. We had packed in a hurry without
much care because we should so soon be unpacking
again. An overhanging branch of a tree had
knocked the van's chimney squint and it hung most
drunkenly to one side; the mattress and its bedclothes looked through the van window. Newtonmore stared at us with unconcealed dislike, and we
hurried through our business to be out of it. We
went a mile along what has become one of the several
Great North Roads since it was tarred but used to
break car springs and be called *The Old Edinburgh*,
a name from the days of the stage-coaches. We
crossed the Spey and turned back on the south side
of the river along a minor road to search for a

camping-place. We found an ideal spot at last, beside a little burn where a sheep-gate opened from the road into moorland country. We could not see a house for miles, which pleased us, for we were shy of neighbours in this disapproving country. So there before us was a camping-place, firewood from a thicket of birches, quietness, and a country as pleasant as Culreoch. Ian hastily swung the car round to enter the gate. Corybante would not quite take the corner, and Ian, forgetting experience, tried to reverse. In a moment we were wedged directly across the road with Corybante's radiator up against one fence and the back of the van against the other. When we said in the same breath *Thank God it's a quiet road without traffic,* a large hackney car loaded with old ladies came round the next bend and drew up in front of us. Desperate situations need desperate remedies; Ian reversed for all he was worth and the fence behind us creaked and groaned, but it gave sufficiently without yielding altogether to let him wrench Corybante round in the direction of the road again. She came almost clear but her mudguard caught in the wires; that was nothing to Corybante; she checked for a moment before all the staples in the fence came out with a mighty *Ping!* and we jumped forward on to the road once more. The van was slightly holed where one of Corybante's rear springs had rammed her when we reversed, but we escaped more easily than we deserved. We went carefully down to

Kingussie to make a circle round the town fountain and return.

We camped, with the burn a few feet from our door. Long rank heather grew round the van wheels. We made a fire and unpacked with the more relief since it was to be our last flitting for a long time. The chimney was battered by the branches which had struck it and the van was dirty once more with soot and oil. We could never have shifted from place to place as we planned. We were glad we had not attempted it. We found a bathing-pool screened by high banks and over-hanging alders. We cleaned the van and mended the chimney before we bathed, and then we splashed about in water as warm as new milk until the kettle boiled. This place was called Inverton, and here we stayed until we were done with the caravan for a year.

INVERTON

INVERTON

Chapter Eight

WE ARE SAVED BY A PUPPY FROM DESPAIR

Our first consignment of fruit was due to reach Kingussie on TUESDAY the TWENTY-SECOND of JULY, a date we had noted in every note-book and diary and calendar we possessed in case we lost our memories and the van went on fire. We had many things to do before that all-important date came round. We sent various news-stories and the daily weather report, a thing which became more difficult instead of easier the longer we kept on sending it; one cannot bring much variety into the terms which describe summer weather within the space of a single line of print, and we wondered when people would become infuriated with our monotonous repetition of the same phrases: *'fine but dull'*; 'dull but warm'; *'warm and sunny'*; 'sunny and warm';—but most important of all our jobs were those that had to do with our real work, the hawking of fruit.

We took our trailer to Kingussie to a joiner who promised and took oaths to have sides made and fitted to it before Saturday morning. The parcels of paper-bags, weights and scales, and the tarpaulin began to arrive at Kingussie station. We left them, meaning to collect them when the fruit came.

On Monday the 21st we went to fetch our trailer to Inverton. It was very gay in fresh green paint, but we had still to paint our name and Corybante's number on it. I love painting with a large wet brush, and I bought a tin of white paint and a paint-brush which Ian said would have done for white-washing, it was so big. I began to picture an entrancing afternoon, for we were going to paint and plan and dream of vast sales.

Ian is always quarrelling with me about my passion for paint and paint-brushes. He was furiously angry because I bought a gallon of varnish and a gallon of oak stain before we left Aberdeen in case the inside of the van needed painting. I must confess that we didn't get much use out of the varnish and the stain until we found a cottage with a plain deal floor. I tried to do the cupboard door in the van, but I gave it up because I couldn't get the colour to match the rest of the van. The door varied from saffron yellow to midnight black, and Ian never forgot to show it to me.

We swept into the station to ask when the goods train from Glasgow arrived in the morning. All at once a porter came running and shouting that there were goods for us.

'What?' we asked, first with astonishment and then with a horrid sinking of the heart.

'Fruit,' he said briefly. Our faces must have

betrayed us for he went on to terrify us even more.

'It came on Saturday,' he said. 'We didn't know where to get hold of you to tell you—I don't know what like it'll be now.'

'It was very hot,' Ian managed to say in a sick voice. 'Aye,' the porter agreed. 'It was bleezing hot in that van.'

We stood for a moment wondering what on earth to do. We knew that our fruit must be ruined; and all our hopes were burst; and all our fine plans broken. I could have sat down and cried.

'Are you taking it now?' the porter enquired.

Ian said, 'We'll just take it.'

We hadn't even got our hawker's licence. We couldn't afford the two guineas to pay for it. The trailer hadn't any name or number. We went desperately down to the goods store and loaded our fruit in its boxes on the trailer. We collected our melancholy little parcels. We drove out of King-ussie, hating it, and went over the Spey in the opposite direction from Inverton, towards Insh. When we found a quiet spot at the roadside we began to unload the fruit and open the cases with oh, such fear. The July sun beat down on our heads. Ian said in a rage, 'Now paint the confounded trailer.'

I began to paint

MACPHERSON, DALWHINNIE

along one side in straggling capitals. We'd made

up our minds to use Dalwhinnie as an accommoda-
tion address on our rounds, because we liked Dalwhinnie and all its people and it wasn't so angry
with us as Newtonmore. And it was far away.

My painting wasn't a success. I couldn't keep
my mind on what I was doing, I couldn't stop
looking to see what Ian was discovering. There
was soon as much paint on my Burberry as on the
trailer. It stayed there for years and years to
remind us of that sad while.

Ian just shut his mouth and went through the
cases of fruit in a blind fury. It was easier to be in
a rage than to think of what it meant to have our
first day ruined. He heaved rotten apples and
oranges into the wood beside the road and wasps
gathered in thousands. I didn't say a word even
when he threw out more than half the case of
Delicious apples; even those that looked sound
were soft or rotten at the heart. The plums were
all in a smush. The Canary bananas seemed to
ripen and rot every moment in the sun. The
oranges were in the best condition except for the
grapefruit, but even they were soft and many of
them rotten.

Ian finished at last, and we looked with dismay
at the remains of all the bonny fruit we had bought
so joyfully. We gathered the straw packing and
began to set fire to it. Suddenly a woman and a
boy came round a corner and approached us shyly.

'Might we have some of the straw?' they asked.

'Ian went through the cases of fruit in a blind fury.'

'You see, our landlady has a puppy and the poor
little thing has no comfortable bed. We were
watching you, and when we saw you burning the
straw we thought you might give it to us, it would
do for the puppy.'

They explained their wish in breathless pauses,
the woman helping the boy out when he stuck
through shyness. Ian made a bundle of the straw
for them.

'Are you selling fruit?' the woman asked with
great diffidence; we said *Yes*, as best we could say it.

'Can I buy oranges?' she asked. 'How much are
they?'

We didn't know but Ian made a lightning guess.
We made our first sale.

We made our first sale! *We could sell fruit!* We
felt that the words should have been blazoned on
the sky. Our saviour bought three shillingsworth
of our fruit, and what was more her purchase put
change in our pocket. She leaned across the trailer
and my wretched printing reprinted itself on her
blue coat, but she laughed at our remorse and told
us how easily she could take the stain out.

I think we sang a little as we went on our road
towards Insh, though Ian was worried because that
wasn't really hawking; it was a gift from the blue;
we'd need to knock at the door for our next customer, and speak to a complete stranger, and
perhaps rouse an angry ogress. We arrived at a
small entrance-lodge at the foot of an avenue. A

'She leaned across the trailer.'

silver-haired old lady answered Ian's knock. He began to tell her that we had cheap good fruit. By bad fortune she asked first about our apples. We had thrown so many away that we had to put a stiff price on them. When she heard the price she laughed an old cynical laugh, the laugh reserved for hawkers, and said 'Cheap!'

Ian was so infuriated that he launched out to tell her that it was cheaper than Kingussie anyway, besides saving her a bus fare. In the end we sold her oranges at a penny each.

She was really impressed by their price, as well she might be, for the rogues of fruit-merchants had sent us a case containing not three hundred oranges but a hundred and seventy-eight. We lost heavily on the case because we fixed the price on the assumption of a three-hundred lot; but what was worse, when we went back to customers who bought them at a penny they were acrimonious about our raising the price. All the same, they were such good, firm, juicy oranges that in the long run people bought them and didn't mind the increased cost, especially as it was still much lower than the local price.

Long and in some cases bitter experience of the Highlands since those days has convinced us that Highlanders like to keep shop and sell things rather than make them; they like being shopkeepers, but they are bad shopkeepers because they would rather make a large profit on a small turnover than a much

larger profit on a large turnover by charging reasonable prices. The consequence is that strangers and
visitors have begun to grudge being done by inefficient local shops and bring their food and stores
with them when they take their holidays. There's
another consequence too arising from high prices
which harms the whole country. If you take eggs,
for example, the prices go away up when the
tourists come; the tourists refuse to be done, and
as a consequence there's no poultry-keeping industry
worth the name in the North. There's no market-
gardening either, but as I've said, Highlanders
would rather sell than grow food any day.

The lady of the lodge became a regular customer
henceforth, and we drove on with gentler thoughts
of the world through an avenue of larch-trees where
the light came green and cool on our hot worried
brows. Ian was in process of discovering that I
couldn't do anything at all with sums involving
half-crowns, so we agreed that I should lure
customers forth and he should do the actual selling.

The road bent and turned, each turn revealing a
view more pretty than the last, and then we were
in the midst of the village of Insh. I did not feel
so bold now about knocking at strange doors as when
I told Ian I preferred doing that to making mistakes
with half-crowns.

We chose a house which looked as if a nice
woman with a kind face owned it. Our clairvoy-
ance was justified. Our new customer was a

darling. She bought our fruit and laughed and
said all of a sudden, 'You'll be a honeymoon
couple.'

We couldn't do anything but gasp and say *Yes*
before we quite knew what we were saying; and
of course that labelled our enterprise in a way Insh
didn't forget.

'I knew it,' she said in triumph. By this time
most of the population of the village was clustering
round our trailer. A woman from Glasgow bought
and bought again.

'God bless Glasgow,' we said, then and afterwards. But Insh equalled Glasgow in its lavishness.
There's only one word to describe its buying—
royal. There was a royal air over the whole place,
especially over the women. I wonder if there's
another place in Scotland where there are so many
regal-looking women on the far side of middle-age?

We left Insh feeling as if we had suddenly come
into an inheritance of friends. The women holding
plates of fruit—for they fetched out plates 'to save
your paper-bags, my dear'—asked when we would
come this way again.

'Friday,' we hazarded, and they stood watching
us until we vanished on the road to Kincraig.

We came there at a very bad time, four o'clock in
the afternoon. All the visitors were out; and the
landladies assured us that they grew their own fruit
and could not say if the visitors wanted fruit or not.
We took house about, and on the whole most people

were pleasant, though some thought that Ian must be a burglar spying out the land. We both had our individual methods of attack. Ian's strong suit lay, I suspected, in flirting with his prospective customers, especially if they were oldish, mine lay in the 'woman to woman' manner. No housewife can help feeling friendly to a creature who prattles about the bother of thinking out dinners, the horrid job it is to wash pans after milk-pudding, especially when you want to be out in the sun, and the blessing fruit is to the busy housewife, saving her work and keeping the family healthy.

Kincraig bought quite a lot though we did come at an inopportune time. We only made one bad break when Ian went to the door of the general merchant's house. Mercifully no one heard him, and he retreated hastily when I called to him in anguished tones to come back because there was a shop next door.

The day was wearing on, and as we reached the main road above the village we felt old in wisdom. We had been snubbed by servant girls, taken into the confidence of visitors, told where there were invalids and where prospective customers; (people were always charmingly pleased to hurry us on to bother their neighbours).

We were tired with all our hurly-burly of emotions and turned Corybante's nose homewards with relief, and content too. In a few hours we had sold thirty shillingsworth of fruit and learned

F

lessons worth pounds. We knew that we had lost
money on our first consignment, but we also knew
that we had too many bananas in one consignment.
And best of all, we knew that there was a market
for our fruit, and our mistakes could be cured.
The query of Kincraig and Insh, 'When are you
coming back?' lay like balm on our souls.

While the kettle boiled on the van stove we
bathed in our pool in the burn. The summer-
scented night came quietly down the hills as we
ate supper at the door of the van and talked of plans
and projects which would make our fortunes.
Grouse called in the heather and trout plopped in
the stream. The day had ended many fears of which
we were scarcely aware but which lay dark in the
back of our minds. There *had* always been the
possibility that not a soul would buy our fruit. We
had not known if we could make people buy, or if
we could even knock at strange doors. We counted
our coppers and slept with quiet minds.

Chapter Nine

WE TAKE STOCK

We were up betimes, and while the porridge hottered away in one casserole and the bacon and eggs in another we took stock of our position. First we made up an order to our Glasgow merchants for a case of oranges, a basket of tomatoes, and a tray of plums. That day we calculated we ought to sell the greater part of our first order. The oranges, thinned by those we flung away, were coming to the bottom of their case; not more than a few pounds remained of our apples, and the plums had gone almost too well.

We thought that they at any rate deserved their going, for at that time plums by no means as luscious as ours were selling in Kingussie shops at 1s. 5d. the pound while we charged but tenpence. All the same we had not expected them to go quite as well as they had. But the fruit we had left made a poor show on the trailer, and people don't buy when they see a thin assortment. We decided it wasn't good business to allow ourselves to run short of our best selling lines.

Our grapefruit and bananas looked like being a dead loss, the first because they were dear and our

best customers were not yet sophisticated into eating
grapefruit; the second because they rotted per-
ceptibly every time we looked at them. So we wrote
an order which tried to keep all these very wise
ideas in mind; and we also sent one of those stiff
notes which Ian delighted to write, asking why the
merchants had behaved so very badly.

When it came to the business of repricing our
wares we had something to go on. We simply
couldn't keep on selling oranges at a penny each.
The case which we counted on holding three
hundred contained exactly a hundred and seventy-
eight. We jumped the price to twopence and
counted on the quality of the oranges to placate our
customers. They were twopence ha'penny everywhere else in Speyside.

The best we could do with our Canary bananas
was to sell them as cheap and fast as we could for
what they would fetch, and buy in less ambitious
quantities another time.

We were terribly hindered by our complete lack
of money. We hadn't enough money to send away
with our order. The takings of the previous day
were six shillings short of the total in our order and
we had petrol and food to buy, besides needing
money for change. But by the grace of goodness
Ian went to the Post Office to send away the
weather-wire and came back with postal orders
which some of his newspapers had sent him. We
scraped together as much as would pay for the

second consignment of fruit; having despatched it, we made forth on our round, going through Kingussie to the little hamlet of Lynchat.

I took the first house and found an old, tall, gray-haired woman sitting in an empty house reading a Bible. She bought tomatoes and oranges and asked when we would come again. We said Thursday on the spur of the moment. Our routes were deciding themselves by sheer guesswork, and that was what came of our intentions to plan so strictly.

She told us that she wouldn't buy apples or plums because her nephew sent her these fruits from the south; and her own apples and plums were ripening on a south wall of her house.

'Too early,' she lamented when she spoke of their ripening. We left her standing with her bowl of fruit at the garden gate, smiling after us. Next door another woman with imitation pearl earrings and a bright superior manner bought nothing and was vulgar. We sold fruit to a woman from Aberdeen who had two thumbs on her right hand. She greeted us with joy.

'You come from Aberdeen,' she stated. 'I knew by your voices.' And she paid us the best compliment we were ever paid in Speyside by asking in a conspiratorial All Aberdonians Together voice how business was going. Obviously she was more interested in the fact that two people whom she could accuse of Aberdeen accents found it worth

while to hawk fruit in Speyside than in all the
mountains and valleys of the Highlands. She
delighted our hearts, which longed for our fruit-
hawking to be taken seriously, by adding:

'Have you a stall in the Castlegate?'

We were sorry we had to say No, we had never
bawled our wares amongst the cheap-jacks and
acetylene flares and drunken pipers and country
geordies and Communists and Salvationists of the
Castlegate.

There were other houses with no visitors in them;
folk shook their heads and said Don't go there; the
summer letting is bad this year; *she* won't have
the money for fruit, and they shooed us past the
houses in which old women wondered how they
were going to get winter past.

In Kincraig Ian marched boldly up to the door of
a private hotel, and was astounded and I must add
shocked to be received with delight. He came back
to parcel up all that remained of our plums and a
couple of dozen bananas and to say that we were
asked to call again; he also said that it was all
damned wrong that a hotel of that size should be
buying haphazard in small quantities from odd
fruit-hawkers and what way was that to run a
business, but that was the Highlands all over,
he'd bet they were even buying their potatoes
from the local grocer by the stone and paying
through the nose for them.

They were! He handed over the fruit and

'An old, tall, gray-haired woman—reading a Bible.'

returned with the news that they wanted us to bring a quotation for potatoes.

As we travelled on towards Aviemore luck played pranks with us; we would sell to every house for miles, and then not a house would buy. I bought pies and bread and butter for our lunch in Aviemore itself while Ian was besieged by Glasgow folk returning from golf or their morning stroll and eager to have fresh fruit at prices which approximated to those with which they were familiar at home. The sight of a policeman reminded us that we hadn't a hawker's licence, so we bolted out of Aviemore and didn't halt till we were across the Spey in Rothiemurchus. We made a fire and tea and counted our money with utter thankfulness. The first day might have been a fluke; this was confirmation of success. We galloped southwards with great expectations, which were very thoroughly disappointed when in seven miles we made not one single sale. Not a soul was patient enough to hear us beyond our first words. Every one said curtly, 'Nothing to-day thanks,' and banged the door. But at last we came to Feshie Bridge, leaving behind the dark spruce woods and the unbuying people who lived in their gloomy depths. The first house at Feshie Bridge bought from us; and so did the second. At the second we were directed a little further on to still another house beside the gorge of the river, where the water thundered and drew us in haste to lean on the parapet of the bridge and stare at the falls. The twisting road passed between a fir wood and a meadow, and the house we sought stood by the meadow. Loud as the water was, you could hear bees in the garden of the house. Blue flowers from that garden hung over the edge of the cliff above the river. A tall woman walked up the garden path wearing a waterproof, incongruous garment on that lovely hot July day, but she wore it gracefully as if she was the elder sister of the lady of Shalott who had in a moment's aberration borrowed a Burberry. She bought apples from us. We carried on towards the dear, kindly, homely village of Insh.

Insh bought from us again though it was only yesterday we were there last. Or was it gossip Insh wanted from us more than squashy apples? An old woman (how many old women we seemed to meet in the Highlands, alas!)—an old woman with no lower teeth asked us for the worst of our apples. Apples, she declared with a kindling eye, were her solace and her joy, but, ah me, what it was to be young! young folk have teeth for apples; dark unlovely age loses its teeth and can't deal with apples. I don't know what her neighbours had told her about our apples to make her desire them, that they were rotten, probably. She munched one of our juiciest apples and talked and gesticulated, while all around her a troop of small children tugged at the skirts of her enormous blue apron and bawled to be given pennies.

The water of the burn made us so fresh again when we reached Inverton that we couldn't stay at rest but set out after an early supper to Dalwhinnie. We stowed the bananas and grapefruit in the back of the car, with little hope of selling them, but we daren't miss a chance to do something about them. We left the trailer at Inverton. There were rough roads ahead, as we found to our cost when we passed through Dalwhinnie and leaving the public road took a private road to Benalder Lodge. Ian had been a ghillie there, and he looked with sorrow at the road which once he had spent days mending. It consisted of two deep ruts separated by a narrow ridge of stone and rock. On one side the hill plunged violently down to Loch Ericht's grim shores; on the other a wooded mountain went as violently up.

Finlay the stalker was glad to see us. He walked round Corybante and told us what she was worth on the strength of his having owned a pre-war B.S.A. motor-cycle. He remarked that it was fool's luck which brought us safely along the road from Dalwhinnie on a car with a broken front spring. Even Ian had no reply to that. Having silenced us, Finlay delicately helped himself to a handful of our bananas.

Ian scarcely recognized the place as the Benalder he knew. Hundreds of navvies swarmed along the lochside making new paths and piers; felling trees and rebuilding houses because the Grampian Elec-

'She munched one of our juiciest apples.'

tricity Scheme was raising the level of the loch by
many feet. Finlay said that *there* was a market
waiting for our fruit; the navvies would buy it!
We did not believe they would but there's no proof
like a trial. We drove Corybante up a steep hill
across a dozen light railway lines. If Finlay had
not reminded us of the broken spring we would
have gone charging ahead, but now we crept
laboriously, listening to every creak, expecting every
jolt to snap the last leaf of the spring and jam the
steering gear and hurl us over a precipice into the
loch.

One could not envy the navvies their camp. It
lay there, 1400 feet above sea level, on a boggy
exposed moor where they slept in tents and fed
in a marquee, in one of the bleakest, rainiest
parts of Scotland. They looked apathetically at
the bananas and with curiosity at the grapefruit.
But as for the bananas they would have none of
them. A dozen dialects recommended Ian to put
the bananas in a hole and stamp on their grave.
Had we tomatoes? (One solitary Glasgow voice.)
Had we tobacco? Had we working shirts? Had
we beer? (A triumphant chorus.)

One of the crowd mothered Ian.

'The firm's feeding us,' he said.

'The firm's . . .' another interrupted.

'Feeding us,' went on Ian's protector firmly.
'They've been giving us banana sandwiches wi'
our pieces till we're scunnered of them.' I

could believe that. I was scunnered of bananas myself.

And yet they actually bought a few dozen bananas and one grapefruit—as an experiment. While we packed up our cases a group of the navvies talked apart and made many motions towards us. Then Ian's interpreter said confidentially, 'Are youse coming regular?' Ian said mebbe. The other pondered.

'It's like this,' he delivered himself at length. 'Me mates is wanting if they could get down the street on a Saturday.'

'You see what I mean,' he said, 'it's too far to walk down and back in that damned sclub dub an' gutter. Now if there was a car making the run——'

Ian said, 'How many would there be going?'

His friend bawled, 'Hey, which of youse chaps wants the run Dalwhinnie Setterday?'

The census was taken by an Irish youth with red hair, freckles, blue eyes, and boots and jacket a size too large for him.

'There'd be two loads for you,' he advised us. 'There's some for Newtonmore coming back Sundays.'

'What's he seeking?' a Scots voice asked warily. Ian made a calculation.

'A shilling each single, one and six return to Dalwhinnie for a full load, four and six return to Newtonmore.'

'Knocking off time's three on Setterday,' we were told. 'You'll be here for sure?'

We would have been elated without a care by this sudden access of good fortune but for Finlay's reminder of the broken spring. We were scared to death by the road, not without good cause. Corybante's lights were feeble and scarcely illumined the road twenty yards ahead. Sheets of muddy water from the cavernous ruts splattered across the headlights and made them dimmer still. We reached Dalwhinnie with relief and astonishment, though goodness knows why we should have been astonished that a car which had carried us so far on such rough roads as Corybante had should have gone six more miles without collapsing.

A car with a broken front axle, a fresh *memento mori,* was completely blocking the railway level-crossing at Dalwhinnie while another car and three gamekeepers tried to drag it away. In a moment our help was requisitioned. We were linked to the rear of the broken car to keep it from digging its nose in the road, a sort of anchor. Corybante's clutch wasn't built for such work, and we went ahead in leaps and bounds which sent the man steering the broken car into a frenzy of apprehension. The village cheered us on our way to the hotel, where we sold more bananas on the strength of our good turn.

It was midnight before we reached Inverton. We had sold two poundsworth of fruit. Most of the over-ripe and spoiled fruit was gone. We knew what were selling lines and what fruit would keep even in hot weather. And most exciting of all, we had an order to taxi navvies, which meant hard cash.

Chapter Ten

WE MEND A SPRING

We were terribly worried by the slap-dash methods of our wholesale fruit-merchant, and though we wrote them pretty forcibly our letters had no effect. We arrived at Kingussie the day after we'd been to Benalder expecting to find our order awaiting us but discovered that only one case of apples had arrived. To this day I can recapture the feeling, half despair, half rage, which overtook us in the dusty July sunshine of that goods yard. The brief northern summer was slipping past, and here we were, forced to let our opportunities go by through no fault of our own. We realized we couldn't possibly go out with a single case of apples and a few grapefruit, so we decided not to make our rounds that day. Instead we took Finlay's words to heart and set about getting our broken spring repaired. This was no easy matter, for every garage in Kingussie was too taken up genuflecting to that race of supermen the Highlanders call Toffs to attend to us. In the end we got the smith at Balgowan, thirteen miles away, to do the job for us.

Whilst Ian jacked Corybante up on her hind legs and the smith hammered away I sat in the daisied

meadows warm in the sunshine, thinking venomously of our perfidious fruit-merchant. But it was
impossible to remain furious long in that place, for
the tinkling of iron, the soft talk of the smith, the
cries of children herding cattle from the corn, all
soothed my irritation away. At last the repair was
done; we paid what I still consider a shockingly
low fee—six and sixpence—and went our way
secure on sound springs. Ian's flannel trousers were
filthy but it was too bonny a day for being angry.

Next morning we set forth again for Kingussie,
confident that by this time our fruit must have
arrived. Alas, we could find neither goods nor
goods-clerk. In a frenzy of anxiety we got hold of
a porter who shook his head at our enquiries. No,
no fruit had come. We resolved to phone to
Glasgow to the merchant, in spite of the cost and
the nervous prostration of a trunk-call south. At
that time there was a gap of thirty miles in the
telephone system along the Great North Road, and
consequently messages from Speyside south had to
be relayed by Grantown, Elgin, and Aberdeen,
through numberless exchanges. Hell had no worse
horror than a phone-call to Glasgow from Kingussie
at the rush hour.

We spent a solid half-hour screaming and listening
and went back to the station no wiser than when we
left it. All we ever heard from Glasgow was *Hallo*.
But when we got to the station we found that our
fruit had arrived after all. It had been there since

G

the previous day. We tried to row the goods-clerk who had caused us bother, worry, and expense. It isn't easy to row a railway official. The clerk assumed an offended virtue as if we were the people to blame.

There was no more zest in the day as we set forth at noon. We knew only too well that it was Friday, the week was almost spent, and here we were loaded down with fruit which would never keep over the week-end. We were too sick even to bother cursing the railway's delays.

And yet the day wasn't quite wasted, nor the week quite ruined. Good luck often smiled on us just when we were in the depths. The hotel at Kincraig had an unexpected influx of visitors and it bought well. Other customers emptied most of our trays of plums and baskets of tomatoes. When we came to Aviemore we were almost able to be happy again. We sold fruit to a picnic party in a little birch wood outside the village. A woman with white hair and bright blue eyes inspected our wares doubtfully. She asked about our apples in a pleasant Irish voice. Her husband was in the fruit-broking business in Belfast (every one we met wasted no time before starting to tell us about themselves!). She bought a whole stone of apples; and oranges; and tomatoes. We forgot our earlier trauchle; we even sang as Corybante bowled along. But on the way back to Insh our singing was suddenly interrupted. As we came round a corner

'Thinking venomously of our perfidious fruit-merchant.'

into a rough patch of road Corybante leaped and
the trailer-pin broke, and with a terrific crash the
trailer went head over heels into the ditch, one
wheel in the air, the other entangled in the fence-
wires. The road was strewn with fruit, baskets,
scales, weights, and paper bags. Oh, our bonny
fruit! There was nothing for it but to get down on
our knees and gather up the remains. Thank
goodness it was a dry day, and the road empty.

We had scarcely spoken about the good-fortune
of capsizing our cargo on a quiet road when cars
laden with old ladies seemed to crowd in on us. We
hastily got the trailer out of the ditch and loaded
with the remains of our fruit under the stare of
critical and impatient eyes. While Ian mended the
trailer-coupling with fence-wire he took from the
fence at the roadside, I dusted the fruit and made it
as fresh as I could. We sold a good deal of it in Insh
without saying anything about its history. I helped
—by eating the plums which had burst. We sold
three pounds' worth of fruit that day, and all that
remained of our morning's consignment was a
dozen or so bananas.

Chapter Eleven

WE CARRY NAVVIES IN MIRY WAYS

The air and the water of Inverton had a tonic
quality which revived our most drooping spirits.
On the Saturday which ended this heart-sick week
we rose gaily to prepare for the day with as much
confidence as if we had met nothing but success.

We had at least gained one thing, ease of mind
with the new spring so that we could travel on the
dreadful Benalder road without fear.

If anything had gone wrong after we left Inverton, I don't know to what depths of despair we'd have
sunk. But luckily the day was fine, the sun shone,
Dalwhinnie was warm and bright for once, and
when we came to that village we were immediately
surrounded by people wanting fruit. We spent the
time there until after midday, and turned at last
to Benalder and our navvies.

The road was even worse than when we saw it
last. The ruts were deeper, with more mud in
them. Corybante splashed the mud into the wind,
which carried it back over us until we were gray
with gutters and looked as little like fruit-sellers
as possible.

Some navvies were still at work along the loch

side and we tried to tempt them to buy our fruit.
But they told us that the time-keeper hadn't
brought their week's wages yet, otherwise we'd
have had a big trade. So they said, and it was
usually the same way. If it wasn't that they had
just sent their money away, or if it was something
other than fruit, we'd have left the place wealthy.
But we sold a few apples at a penny each and
tomatoes by auction, charging from a ha'penny to
twopence according to size. They had a passion
for tomatoes and ate them all at one bite. Our
pockets filled with coppers, and we found that we
had sold thirty-two shillings' worth of the relics of
our fruit to Dalwhinnie and the navvies. The last
of our bananas were gone!

We waited at Benalder Lodge until the shift came
off work. A launch-load of men from the far end
of the loch nine or ten miles away came ashore
hunting for provisions which had failed to reach
them. They commandeered Corybante to carry
their sacks of bread and potatoes and beer-bottles
down to the boat. The eggs were broken amongst
the bread before they ever got on to the launch.

Ian took five navvies to Dalwhinnie at five o'clock,
and three tradesmen went with him to Newtonmore. He promised to fetch them back again on
the Sunday night. We didn't know the exact law
about the taxying business, but just in case of
trouble we asked the men to pay us discreetly. For
the rest of the time that we taxied them Ian was for

ever being taken furtively into quiet corners by navvies who slipped their fare into his hand with nods and winks and conspiratorial looks.

They never had the slightest doubt about Ian's ability to get them down to Dalwhinnie or back, which certainly made driving easier for him. No matter what happened, though the car skidded from one side to another, now overhanging the edge of the precipice which went down to the loch, now making as if to climb the mountain, the navvies never murmured, or if they did make a sound it was to cheer Corybante's acrobatics. One would think the tricks she did were specially for their benefit, they liked them so much. But mostly they spent the time deep in conversations about other jobs they'd been on here and there throughout Britain and, indeed, throughout the world; or else they made cryptic remarks about compressors and gangers and culverts, although one man did once get such a fright that he jumped over the back of the car into the gutters of the road. His mates wouldn't let him back again and he was forced to walk to Dalwhinnie. He spent most of the night with his money in his hand searching for Ian to pay him and tell him that he didn't mean to bilk him by jumping out.

By the time Ian returned from Newtonmore, his five passengers had collected three others who wished to go to Benalder. They were very excited; two old gray-heads chanted an Irish rebel song, a

Glasgow man sang the Red Flag, two others hastily fell asleep. They gave Ian drinks out of their beer and whisky bottles and leaned over his shoulder to help him to drive. It was funny to remember that only a month ago he was correcting exam. papers for undergraduates.

We reached Inverton at midnight and made porridge and ate it with milk and slept like logs. The water and the air refreshed us to face the Benalder road once more. We had earned more than a pound by our taxi-driving. We had booked not one but *three* car-loads for next week-end, and a load was a load when Corybante took it. There was no limit except space to what she would carry. The heavier we loaded her the better she went through the mire to Benalder. But we were glad that Monday was free, for we were very tired.

'They never had the slightest doubt about
Ian's ability.'

Chapter Twelve

WE HAVE GOOD INTENTIONS AND NEW NEIGHBOURS

So that was a week, and we could sit down to talk it over and speak of weeks to come. We got into touch with firms of fruit-merchants recommended by a trade journal and obtained quotations for fruit from Glasgow and Perth and Inverness. We had to work out the final cost of the fruit from these towns by taking account of railway charges, and we felt most businesslike as we saved pennies here and sixpences there. We found that Glasgow firms were generally cheaper than those in Perth and Inverness, but the extra carriage from Glasgow raised prices on bulky stuff until it was dearer in the end. Ian caught fingerling trout, which we ate, heads, bones, tails and all while we discussed our daily journeys for the future.

Monday was to be a clear day. We'd had enough of fruit, which lay in a goods shed over the week-end. We needed a day in which to make up our accounts, such as they were, to send off news we'd gleaned throughout the week, and to tidy the caravan. We had far too many things and far too various an assortment of things in the van, and Ian's type-

writer and fishing-tackle and my clothes and the
dinner dishes were always getting into a complete
confusion.   Then Corybante demanded to be rested
and greased sometimes.

Tuesday was already committed to the villages of
Lynchat, Kincraig, and Insh, a pleasant day with
an easy journey of about twenty miles.   Wednesday
was Aviemore and Feshie Bridge's day.   We hoped
to sell tremendous quantities of fruit on Wednesday.
It had already been kind to us and a good deal of its
territory was still unconquered, by us at least.   We
proposed to push beyond Aviemore to shooting-
lodges, farms, and crofts on both sides of the Spey.

We mapped out a route for Thursday which
would take us to the outskirts of Grantown along
the north bank of the Spey, and home again through
Nethy Bridge and the moors of Tulloch.   This most
ambitious journey would carry us seventy miles in
one day, and we were sure that when we taught
the country how useful we were, then we'd be
doing a hundred miles a day.   On Friday we were
again committed to Kincraig and Insh.   Dalwhinnie
could have Saturday forenoon, and the afternoon
and evening were devoted to taxying our navvies.
We must fetch masons and joiners back to Benalder
on Sunday from their homes in Newtonmore.   The
weather report was every day's job.

People had asked for vegetables, so we ordered
potatoes, onions, and carrots.   We would gladly
have carried green vegetables also but the railway

freight on them was prohibitive. There was no
market-garden within fifty miles of Newtonmore
—appalling thought. But that is all one thing with
the Highlander's lust for shopkeeping and dislike
or inability to make what the shopkeeper sells. It
seems no crofter or farmer or any one else in Speyside can be bothered digging and planting and
growing flowers and vegetables and fruit even
though the country is full of people yearning for
fresh vegetables every summer. You've got to go
to a city to get a decent supply of fresh green stuff
and flowers.

There are scarcely any proper household gardens
even through most of the Highlands. Hens,
flowers, and vegetables, which Lowlanders find
very profitable affairs, are despised by the proud
Highlander as women's work—work is the operative
word; he will condescend to keep bees so long as
they keep themselves. We sometimes visited a
crofter friend of Ian's and took his wife a vegetable
as a most welcome luxury! In the south, in Dum-
friesshire, for example, every cottar house has its
garden with its precious flowers, but the Highlands
have their scenery of course; Nature adorns the
land and Covent Garden or Glasgow provides the
Brussels Sprouts. When people talk to us about
making the Highlands prosperous we remember
the cabbages we couldn't buy anywhere nearer
than Perth, and wonder.

Monday didn't prove quite the empty silent day

we expected. A Ford lorry with a green canvas hood came through our gate in the mid-afternoon, and drove past our van. 'Food for a sheep-clipping,' said Ian with an infuriating air of knowledge-ability. 'Tinks,' said I. We were both wrong. In the evening Ian conquered his anger over the trespass on our peace sufficiently to go to the lorry to borrow matches. A man and wife were lying shivering in bunks under the canvas hood, with their clothes on, but very cold nevertheless. Ian invited them to come and have coffee, but really to see how clever we were to have a real caravan with a fire and proper beds instead of a makeshift lorry. They charmed us by admiring everything. The husband had roughed it in all parts of the world and his wife didn't care to say straight out that the lorry was cold and uncomfortable for a holiday, especially when the east wind blew as it did this night.

While we were telling them how quiet it was here, and that they were the first people to come through the gate since we arrived, another caravan halted in the bay of the gate. It was a very flashy little affair compared with our huge home. It was streamlined and painted black and cream, and it had imitation leaded windows; it was the very sort of thing that people accustomed to living in a tiny modern bungalow would buy to make them feel they were still at home when they were away from it in the wilds.

A figure which looked like a seven-foot boy scout, dressed in very skimpy shorts, a khaki shirt, and green stockings, hopped out of the car and leaped the gate to come towards us.

'Ah, excuse me,' he stated as he approached, 'but ah you will undahstand that I am not intruding in any way upon a private camping-ground—ah I have no wish to intrude—I have camped heah each yeah wheah you are—' he glowered at us as if we should have known that this was his camping-ground—'each yeah—the only dem camping-place between heah and Fortingall shall we say?'

When we failed to reply he went on in rapid, strident tones: 'When I saw the caw—the caw and the ah—van—I thought it was a tinkah camp, by jove, a tinkah camp. I camp heah every yeah—'

'We are tinkers,' said Ian unpleasantly.

'Ah,' the crow-throated visitation said, 'as I was saying I thought it was a tinkah-camp when I saw the ah—van and caw—I say, I find the best mannah in dealing with tinkahs is to give them a shilling—which ah ensuahs their guarding your caravan—'

Ian glared at him until I began to fear a breach of the peace, but the stranger was utterly unaware that he could possibly be giving offence—unaware or heedless. He departed as precipitately as he arrived. In a few seconds he was climbing the tree beside the gate; an instant later he had drawn a wireless aerial from the top of the tree to his caravan. Then he brought a meat-safe from the van, and a spade. It was nearly midnight and we decided he was drunk. It would have been quite easy just to let Corybante touch the van as we went out next morning. It did not look very stable on its patent telescopic legs. He was gone by night, to Fortingal no doubt, with his spade, his aerial, his method for tinkahs, his safe, and his wife in the background, one of the Empire busters.

Chapter Thirteen

WE MAKE MANY FRIENDS AND SOME MONEY

The circuit by Lynchat, Kincraig, and Insh was short but it gave us a regular trade of about three pounds a day, and it was never done revealing new and charming facets. There was, for example, a small house in Lynchat where knocking brought no reply; when we tried the handle of its door, it was always locked. Now in Lynchat we had to make a circle because the village was built along the main road, and then it followed a steep grassy track which climbed from the main road for about a hundred yards and descended to the trunk road again. (We bogged Corybante there when the rains began.) Well, as sure as we completed our round of the village and came down past the empty little house a second time, its door would be open and an old woman waiting in it to halt us with a stern hand. And behind her waited an impatient cohort of small children who were not allowed to budge until she had bought plums or sampled our pears in case they were hard. Her buying over, the children came out in a stream with grown-ups following them to treat the bairns to fruit. Yet all

the time, even when the old lady, with her apron
full of plums, waved us farewell and all the children
shouted, the house behind them looked blind and
vacant, as if it were no more than a blank wall
with no house at its back. But the money we got
from the old woman and her retinue never changed
into straw and dry leaves so far as we heard, and
I am sure the bank would have told us.

Ian knew the Spey of old, but I was a stranger to
its valley, and I could never get over being astonished when I saw how sluggish a stagnant stream
it really was. I had been taught in my own school-
days that it was the most rapid river in Scotland,
and I suppose I had told my pupils the same thing
when it came my turn to teach. And here beneath
my eyes it was a dull currentless ditch for almost
thirty miles, without motion and with very little
beauty. All along the roadside from Kingussie to
Kincraig there were pools of standing water and
wide fields of reeds and rushes with here and there
a drowned tree; the railway on its embankment
ran through a morass. Scum and water weeds,
jungles of stunted willows, thickets of flags, reached
all across the valley. If it had not been for the hills
on either hand, the magnificent Cairngorms on one
side and the wooded lower slopes of the Monadhliaths on the other, the valley of the Spey would have
been an intolerable desolation. The swiftest river
forsooth! I began to suspect a good deal of the
information I had passed on so glibly to my pupils.

H

We often gathered mushrooms to carry home
with us and sold them before we had gone a mile.
They grew in the woods near Kincraig, but we
had to hurry to get them before the sun rose or the
cows ate them. Many of our customers told us that
they loved mushrooms and we fetched some for
them, but we were careful not to say they had
grown at their back door. The sixpences might as
well be in our pockets as theirs, we argued.

Kincraig met us crying for fruit. Our hotel
increased its purchases until it was buying fruit by
the stone and potatoes by the hundredweight. But
a pretty little wooden house which stood under the
shadow of the hotel never deviated from buying
one half-pound of tomatoes.

We were strictly determined to sell the best we
could as cheaply as we could. When people came
eagerly to us and told us they had been waiting for
us we were glad. We were doing a useful job, and
we were helping not only ourselves but all the folk
who grew the fruit and vegetables we sold. It was
better to our minds if we made the same profit on
a large turnover as we could have made on a smaller
turnover by putting up our prices, because our
customers had more for the same money, we had
as much, and the folk who produced the sweets of
the earth enjoyed a larger market.

Kincraig tumbles from the main road down a very
steep hill to the Spey, and its head-over-heels main
street was always on the point of carrying Corybante

with it in spite of her brakes. We began to carry chock-blocks for her wheels. We were becoming very efficient, and people admired the alacrity with which Ian leapt from the car to chock the wheels.

We discovered by accident a thing we should have discovered by the light of reason. But most of our useful discoveries were by accident. A house at the ridge of the brae which ran down through Kincraig to the river had met us every day in July with a shaken head. No fruit, its folk said. When August came we did not dream there would be any alteration. One morning, while we were selling our half-pound of tomatoes to the house beside the hotel, a grave-faced woman halted beside our trailer to survey our fruit. The man who accompanied her stood by with an air of detached amusement. He whistled, jingled money in his pocket, smiled into his beard, and looked this way and that, every way but at the trailer, with the air of a thoroughly impatient and restless man being patient. He wore a suit of blue Harris tweed. His wife pored over our merchandise with gravity and silence which seemed to become excited but was still controlled. When we had weighed the half-pound of tomatoes into the customary bowl, and said good-bye to our friends from the wooden house, she said, 'You sell?'

The man with the beard smiled and nodded and looked over her head at the clouds with an *I told you so* manner.

'What are your prices?' she went on.

We told her and she said, Leave so much of this and so much of that at the little house round the corner. It was the house we had given up visiting; she and her husband were the new tenants. Of course, we thought, people take houses for a month and our reception in July means nothing in August. We said Yes, most gladly. But when we turned the corner to leave the fruit and vegetables she ordered her husband was at our heels.

'Melons?' he said, looking at those we had bought on spec. 'Are they ripe?'

Ian pressed them with his thumbs to show that they were. The other shook his head.

'I've seen that done before,' he said. 'It doesn't mean anything. The melons I've bought since I came were all as hard as turnips. Well, I might add one of yours to my collection. Is the sun going to shine? *That* might ripen them. Oh, give me two.'

When we came that way again we found that the melons hadn't graced his collection for long. They were ripe and he ate them.

'They were fairish,' he admitted, and we tried to visualize him eating them. To eat melons with a beard must be a difficult business. Meanwhile, his wife, together with her cook and a maid, held anxious consultations over the trailer arguing whether to buy three pounds of carrots or four, and if the apple tart would suffice for the morrow

'The air of a thoroughly impatient man being patient.'

without extra fruit, and which was best value,
plums or grapefruit. The cook adored mushrooms,
so we gave her a few that we had gathered and told
her in the strictest privacy where to find more if
she went before the cows were let out of their byres.

Sally Brown lived next door. That was not her
name, it was the name we bestowed on her when
we saw her first of all. She arrived with her
husband at the gate into our camping-ground one
day, and while her husband tried to catch Ian's
trout in our burn, she legged it back and fore along
the road like a colt, or leaned against the old
Renault in which they arrived, or stood beside the
burn glooming into its pools. She smoked con-
tinually, and she was so tall and saturnine and mock-
mannish that we remembered the shanty and sang
in her honour:

> Sally Brown 's a fair young maiden,
>   Way hey roll and go,
> She drinks rum and chews tobacco,
>   Put my money on Sally Brown.

as we went towards Newtonmore to send our
weather report.

She lived next door to the man in blue Harris
who collected melons. Whenever we arrived at her
door her cook came out first; she was a small round
woman with a Yorkshire accent and an outrageous
tongue; next came the cook's husband, and he was
old, with a smooth pink and white complexion like
a boy. He dropped the pruning-shears or the silver

'Stood beside the burn glooming into its pools.'

(for he was butler too) or whatever he had in his
hands, to follow his wife; and when he saw who
we were he trotted back into the house for his
mistress. So there we all were, set for a little light
conversation. The cook told us what new theories
Sally Brown and her husband had been having
about us during the past few days. Ian was a cut
above the common in their opinion, and especially
in Sally Brown's. She had a romantic mind, and
I caught her looking very speculatively at me as if
she thought it was my doing that brought him so
low as to hawk fruit.

They seemed to spend a lot of time amusing
themselves concocting fairy-tales about Ian. He
was doing it to earn his way through a University.
He had lost his money. He was a poor student—
encumbered by a wife, you could feel they suspected
that.

We were brother and sister at first, but it was a
great relief to the cook when she discovered the
truth. Then her conversation became thoroughly
bawdy. She rattled on like a modern Wife of Bath
while Sally Brown bawled out remarks about the
passers-by. The whole scene was most regrettable.

Sally Brown was a curious woman to be so set
on speaking in a deep voice and striding about like
a man. She had nice white hands on which I know
she must have spent a lot of care; her voice was
pretty when she forgot to try to growl with it. In
the middle of straddling the garden path with her

hands thrust deep in the side pockets of her tweed skirt she would rush into the house to return with a jumper she had knitted herself and which she would insist on trying on there before all onlookers for us to admire. She wore a shirt blouse with a neatly knotted tie—unlike Ian's, which she insisted it was her duty to put right. She would chase him round and round the trailer and across her lawn with the eager eye of a mother hunting down a child with a bubbly nose. She carried money loose in her pockets and jingled it like her manly neighbour the melon-hunter, but when she paid us it was from a purse she kept in the house—probably under a bowl or in a drawer.

Huge brogues and thick woollen stockings couldn't make her legs look masculine, for she had most neat ankles and feet. She wore her hair long with a net to keep its brown masses together. The black velvet band round her forehead was no darker or more velvety than her eyes, except when those eyes shone fiercely upon Ian's untidy tie and creased old jacket.

She was never done telling us tales of her Aunt Kate who stayed with her, and she wouldn't buy grapefruit because, she said, her house was bung full of greedy relatives, damn their eyes and souls, and what the hell did we think she was anyway, *made* of money, to be giving *them* grapefruit? The cook interjected ribaldries into the angry flood and the gardener-butler with his shining gentle face beamed at his Rabelaisian wife or gave Cockney

explanations and elaborations of her more abstruse
ribaldries.

'Six cousins with bellies like vacuum-cleaners,
all sitting eating my food! "Aunt Kate," says they,
"you never saw Jenny eating so well at home."
"I couldn't afford it," says Aunt Kate. Damn
them, *my* food! they might have the decency to
gobble without gloating about it,' cried Sally Brown.
The Wife of Bath advised us to get a settled job.
A respectable woman passed by. 'That woman is
going to be sick,' vociferated Sally Brown. The
cook regretted that she couldn't buy any more
fruit this day.

We were confessors and guide-books to half
Kincraig. A superior visitor disdained to buy; she
dealt with *shops*, she told us with a heavy English
accent. But if we cut our prices by half—and
could we suggest any burns where her husband
would get free fishing? She spent a penny on a
turnip. When she and her two impertinent small
sons had gone, her maid came forth with sixpence
to buy bananas—'one for me and one for Jeannie
in the kitchen and two for Mary on the hill.' We
heard all about her own and her friends' young men,
and all about their jobs. The smooth face that the
fronts of houses turned to the world was not
always evidence of peace within.

Kincraig, and every village, had its bush telegraph. All the tittle-tattle of the place went like
lightning in the mouths of maids and message-boys.

We sold bananas regularly to a house just beyond Kincraig. It was inhabited by a chauffeur, his wife, and a lovely wolf-hound. But Ian spoiled that trade by offering to swop Corybante for the Rolls the shuvver drove. It is not wise to try to jest about the gods of locomotion with their priests.

The road to Insh went through the woods like Pan, dancing. But we insulted Insh, which we loved, almost to death. A house at the east end of the village bought so well that one day we decided to pass it because it must be tiring of its extravagance. The folk had been waiting for us, and watching for us, and they kept our lapse up against us for many a long day.

When we entered the village it simply stopped work, even in hay-time, when men, women, and children were busy in the little fields around the houses. Old men perched on the heads of haystacks sent children to buy an apple or a plum for them and cried gossip to us while they waited for the fruit. Stout, handsome, muscular women who balanced themselves with the aid of a hay-fork on the summit of vast cart-loads of hay took advantage of the stack-builders' preoccupation with us to cry to each other from peak to peak. They rested and wiped their red cheeks with their blue aprons. Their arms were bare and their faces shone and their hair shone in the sun, for Insh seemed to be full of black-haired women.

Now and then we found the village deserted and

every house empty except for one where a cripple
boy waited with a penny clutched in his hot palm
to buy an apple with—like the cripple left in
Hamelin; but it was cranberries, not a piper, that
seduced the folk, and everybody went away, women
and children too. There was nothing to do then
but wait till the berry-pickers came home again
with their knitting, though how they hoped to knit
and gather berries too we could not understand.
Perhaps they knitted charms for eternal youth into
their one purl two plain.

Once the village astounded us with an immense
order for bananas. We asked why, and were told
a wedding-feast. We insisted on contributing something, so they chose oranges, which we would never
have dreamed of suggesting for a Highland wed-
ding. Echoes of that wedding-feast rumbled
through Insh and met us for ages afterwards,
together with a good deal of frank chat from the
knitters in the sun which sent us blushing out of
the village.

Blushing was no longer our easiest task. We
were becoming hardened hawkers, and Ian did not
even blench when Insh began to tell him that he
was related by blood with half its people. There
were family Bibles for proof, though some of the
relationships were too confidential for any Bible.
Amongst the genealogical details which so enchant
Highlanders we heard it interjected that the fruit-
merchants in Kingussie said our fruit was too cheap

'Sent children to buy an apple or a plum for them.'

to be good. But Insh was satisfied and told the
shopkeepers so. We delighted in the news.

Every day we came through Insh, sunny, knitting, holding wedding-feasts and inquests on
wedding-feasts, we liked it better.

Chapter Fourteen

WE TAKE FIVE POUNDS IN A DAY

The circuit by Aviemore, which we extended east to Nethy Bridge, was our best day's run. On it we first topped the five-pound mark which we had set as a goal without ever expecting to come near it. But we sold more than five pounds' worth of fruit frequently on a Wednesday, with the result that we were often short of stock for Thursday.

Five pounds' worth of fruit was an amazingly large quantity. We set out in the morning with both the trailer and the back of the car loaded, yet we returned almost empty.

We were busily learning new tricks in our trade, which increased our turnover and our profits while they earned us new customers. We studied our price-lists with the most extreme care in order to discover 'selling lines' (for we had even begun to speak the jargon of trade). We found, for example, that cooking pears were very cheap indeed. Now cooking pears were novel as well as good. But when our pears arrived and we put our teeth in them—we were always only too willing to be our own best customers—they were so sweet and juicy that we sold them as cooking pears which could be eaten raw. We got rid of a whole bushel-barrel in a forenoon and made ten shillings on it. We sold several barrels as fast as we could handle them after that. People asked for our pears.

The pears taught us that there was a demand for cheap cooking fruits. We had been selling Californian plums at a keen price and a very small profit, which was always liable to vanish because these plums were dear, and easily damaged, and difficult to weigh into exact pounds and half-pounds. We laid in a stock of cherry plums and Victoria plums instead. The cherry plums were a little cheaper to buy from the merchants than the Victorias, but we could sell them dearer because, like the pears, they were ripe and sweet enough to eat uncooked.

Now people began to place orders with us for fruits for jam, plums by the stone and cooking apples too. Our profits let us view Corybante's appetite with equanimity. She only did fifteen miles to the gallon. Ian assured me he would attend to that, and he spent a whole Monday fiddling with jets. The consequence was that Corybante travelled twenty-nine miles on her next four gallons, so Ian hastily hid the note-book in which he marked down our mileage and the petrol we used, and put the jets back as they were at first.

We were so busy selling on the Aviemore route that we had no time to gossip and make friends with the people as we did in Lynchat, Kincraig, and Insh. But there were many houses which received us amiably for our news. One old lady was so delighted to see DALWHINNIE on the trailer (which village we chose because we fondly hoped it would not attract much questioning) that she greeted me with a barrage of questions about old Craib—whose name I had never heard till then. Ian rescued me and parried the questions, but our customer was very dissatisfied with us.

Hotels were very profitable customers. Lynwilg Hotel surrounded us with people eager for fruit. The maids bought melons, the proprietor oranges for his wife, the barmaid grapefruit to keep her slim, and a couple of men who were driving a beer-lorry bought bananas. The proprietor used to lead Ian round a corner to advise him that green vegetables were the things to sell, and he could buy them at the weekly auction in Inverness. We ought to go there on Fridays, when vegetables were sold at the mart, and hawk what we bought all the way home. Had the Market been on Monday, or any other day than Friday, we would have tried out his advice.

Aviemore itself was always a dull market. We did find a few good customers. But as time wore on into August, Glasgow visitors departed and were replaced by people from Edinburgh, and Edinburgh, you will understand, buys not from hawkers when shops, though dear and not so well supplied, are

I

stationary. Edinburgh loves the immobile and
established, statuesque and statutory.

But boarding-houses and hotels dealt with us
though scarcely a single private house spoke us
civilly.

A few miles beyond Aviemore we had an Irish
customer. She lived in a cottage by the roadside,
with the railway, on which her man worked,
behind. She was little and dark, pleasant of face
and kindly, and she told us all about herself. She
came from Ireland when she was a girl and she had
wandered all round the world before settling here,
a girl no longer. In spite of her far-travelling, her
brogue was as if it came newly from Ireland.

We sold her tomatoes and apples—Dutch tomatoes. She liked Scotch tomatoes but the price was
too dear. We made our fire at midday on the other
side of the road from her house, to boil our kettle
and make tea as we did every day. We asked her
where we could get water. She insisted on filling
our kettle, and it was with rather a conscience-
stricken appreciation we discovered afterwards that
she had to carry every drop of drinking-water from
Loch Vaa, two or three hundred yards off, over two
fences and across a hill.

Her house was at the edge of the wooded rolling
country in whose centre we had camped at Culreoch.
East went the fir woods, and to the west were
steeper woods of birch; the valley narrowed west-
wards until it passed under the shadow of Craigel-

lachie and the two mountain ranges at Aviemore. We sat by our fire, looking all around with pleasant content while the Irishwoman told us about foreign parts of the world where she had been. A little patch of garden overgrown with Pink Fire lay behind her like the glowing years of her youth which she called up to mind. She wore heavy boots with tackets in their soles. They were none too heavy for the work she did, in her garden, and drawing water and carting birch-branches from the woods. Her thick brown hair, like Sally Brown's, was covered with a net. She asked us where we made calls and recommended houses to us in which we would be sure to find customers. Every time we called she had the names of new customers for us.

A little farther on in Kinveachy we discussed apples with another old woman. She knew all about Sturmers, Pippins, windfalls, and orchards, but she bought our American fruit nevertheless. We went home by Inverdruie on the other side of the Spey from Aviemore, taking orders for jam-jars to hold the jam that housewives would make with our plums as we went, and that was Wednesday with its five pounds.

We tried hard to be solemn about Thursday, but to the very end of our fruit-hawking its journey was in reality a long picnic-jaunt. We did sell a good deal of fruit, as well we might when our petrol for the day cost ten shillings. Every Wednesday night as we counted our takings we decided that there was more real satisfaction in a hard profitable day's work than in any gallivanting; and every Thursday was like every past Thursday.

We took enormous pains preparing for the day. We laid out our kettle, our tea and sugar and milk; we rolled up towels to dry us after we bathed in some warm loch in Tulloch. Then as if by afterthought we'd heap the fruit anyhow in the trailer and depart like children for a joy-ride.

We began a most involved business affair at the scrap of village called Drumullie, half-way between Aviemore and Grantown, on this Thursday round. A very stout and amiable woman bought fruit regularly until one day she suggested it was our turn to buy from her. We asked what she had to sell. She fetched a huge lovely basket of cranberries. The children had gathered them. Was fourpence a pound too much?

Ian swears that he weighed that basket of cranberries exactly and it was ten pounds, but the fact remains that by the end of the day we had sold twelve pounds of berries from it.

When we told the stout lady she said neither yea nor nay, she had no reproaches to make; she simply produced another even larger basket, and asked for its value in apples and plums. She went further and told us how to clean the berries of leaves and dust. You take your basket to a clean grassy hillock, and spread there on the ground the sheet which you have fetched from your linen cupboard. The

'Pink Fire lay behind her like the glowing years of
her youth.'

day should be dry with a brisk but not violent breeze. Having laid stones at each corner of the sheet to hold it down, you let the cranberries fall from their basket in a thin steady stream from a height of two feet or so. The wind winnows them, and all the dust and leaves and sticks of heather are blown away.

Our melon-collector in Kincraig was so delighted to hear of this trick that he bought all the cranberries we had with us, and in a moment we saw him depart with a sheet under one arm to do his winnowing before the morning breeze fell. We went next door and asked Sally Brown if she had ever eaten cranberry jam, or apple and cranberry tart (than which there is no nicer). She said No, what were cranberries? We praised the jam and the tarts, and explained how to winnow the berries. The cook conferred with her mistress. Yes, they said, give us half a stone of cooking apples. We must try these tarts. As we weighed out the apples the cook said sneeringly, 'Did you call those apples?'

'Now the cranberries,' said Sally Brown. But of course we had sold them all. Those berries seemed to involve us in a great deal of sharp practice.

We went from Drumullie to Nethy Bridge. The boy who watched the petrol pump was a regular customer for one banana. We sold melons to houses where there were children. But except for these, and an old lady who bought plums for the

children and apples for the dog, Nethy was un-
profitable. Yet we never grudged our visit. We
bought our week's bread there from a bakehouse
whose cakes made Thursday's picnic a delight.

Ian tried to tell the baker how much he liked his
bread, and almost had his nose snapped off for his
pains. But Nethy *did* have strange shops: its
bakery, with lovely bread and short manners; its
shoemaker's shop on the outskirts of the village, a
dark-windowed little place with this strange sign,

BOOTS REPAIRED FREE TO-MORROW,

and another sign underneath

Honey for Sale.

We went in to look for the shoemaker, intending
to buy honey, but we never found him at work or
in his shop. It was always empty and when we
had gazed at the brass nails hammered into the
leather seats of stools in the outline shape of sailing-
ships we would go boldly through this place where
it was always afternoon, and never to-morrow, to
gaze out at its back door upon a queer embroiled
garden with stairs climbing up to lofts and dovecots.
The smell of honey and the noise of bees came from
one corner, from another the odours of a farm-yard
confusedly mixed with the scent of flowers. But
no one was to be seen and we never succeeded in
buying honey there.

Our Thursday afternoons were spent amongst the
moors of Tulloch. We bathed in sea-blue Loch

Mallachie while wasps guarded our fruit. There were few customers, but the sun shone on the wide miles of empty country. A woman from California grew homesick over our plums and grapefruit; the Street of Kincardine with its five lonely houses sampled our pears; we sold three or four pounds of fruit; and we picnicked amongst the juniper-smelling reaches of Tulloch whence we carried home fresh vigour for the labour of the week-end. On Thursdays we were free from care; we picnicked and we bathed, and like the old round earth, adored the sun.

Chapter Fifteen

WE RAISE A GHOST

Friday was busy with Kincraig and Insh and preparations for Saturday. Dalwhinnie occupied us on Saturday forenoon. We did not go from house to house but drew up at the petrol station, where people with time on their hands seemed always to be gathered. The petrol pumps were opposite the police station, but we took the risk of being asked for our hawker's licence and sold the policeman enormous quantities of carrots, which he bought in the most shamefaced way while the villagers shouted with joy and bade him buy more and keep his back up; they advised us with ribald guffaws that he was newly married. It seems that carrots are a nerve food, in Dalwhinnie at any rate.

We left the trailer at Inverton on Saturdays and carried our crates and baskets and boxes and scales and bags and everything else in the back of the car. But Dalwhinnie had endless patience and plenty of time to spare. No one grumbled though we were slow in serving our customers. August was rainy everywhere but it was torrential in Dalwhinnie. Yet the folk would stand bareheaded in the deluge waiting patiently while Ian grobbled about in the

back of the car for what they wanted. We grew
to be very fond of Dalwhinnie. It was even franker
of speech than Insh.

The wives of Aberdonian wood-cutters bought
potatoes and carrots and onions from us as we went
along the Benalder road. They invariably told us
that we were rogues and sharks, our prices were
criminal, and if we had tried to charge them similar
prices in Aberdeenshire they'd have had us taken
up for extortion. They said all this with the
angriest voices and then bought generously so that
we never knew whether they were being angry or
merely keeping up their hearts in a foreign land
where it was necessary to impress the natives. We
became quite good at their own game and miscalled
them as heartily as they miscalled us. Did they
expect mealy potatoes for a gift? we demanded.
If you live in a God-forsaken wilderness you can't
expect city prices, we said. Perhaps they'd rather
deal with the grocers' vans. They should have
stayed in Aberdeenshire.

The navvies had not recovered, and never would
recover, from their prejudice against bananas.
They were good customers for all the other fruit.
Gangs of them were still at work along the lochside
on the steep slopes of the hill as we went towards
Benalder. When they saw us coming they would
bawl 'Hey!' and gallop down the hill, or up the
hill, to stop us and make a ring round us. Their
picks and shovels and sticks of gelignite got leave

'Carrots which he bought in the most
shamefaced way.'

to lie until they had made us take every case of fruit
out of the back seat so that they could finger the
plums to see if they were ripe, and choose the
squashiest tomatoes. Their gangers would bawl in
vain for them to come back to work. You could
hear irate voices calling 'Hey, youse, where'n hell
you think you're going?' Then the anger would
disappear from the voices and the gangers would
begin to plead, cajoling the men, 'Come on, boys,
it's no' breaking-off time yet.' They coaxed in vain.
At last they would drag their feet to the road and
accept small gifts of tomatoes and oranges from their
insubordinate gangs.

Fortunately for us the navvies preferred their
fruit to be overripe and we got rid of all the week's
leavings on them, selling tomatoes one at a time,
penny ha'penny for a very big one, penny for an
average size, and two a penny for what the navvies
called the little chats. We sold our apples at a
penny the piece. The men were shy at first to eat
plums; they weren't a manly fruit. But they
overcame their shyness. It was a pretty sight to see
them all clustered round the car *sooking* away at
plums and oranges and commending their mates
a mile away to come and buy in the loudest of
bawls; 'Hey you, Jock, come'n get an aipple!'

The motherly spirit was very strong in them.
Every time we appeared one or another would take
Ian aside to advise him to bring eggs next time,
or working-clothes, or tobacco. But they were as

'They made us take every case of fruit out.'

ready to give each other advice.   An oldish man
with very ill-fitting false teeth bought a dozen
oranges and made a virtue of his necessity by
declaring to all and sundry that they were missing
a treat by choosing apples instead of oranges.
Occasionally a boat-party going west to the head of
the loch drew inshore to see what was happening.
Then one or two messengers would come flying up
the hill to buy fruit and vegetables; they were
feeding themselves, they said.   And when we asked
where they were going they answered with pride,
'All the way to the Ghost House'.

We began to hear a great deal about this Ghost
House.   The story of its haunting grew until we
scarcely recognized the tale which we ourselves
helped to create.

Ian must have some of the credit—or the blame
—for setting the story rolling which filled the Ghost
House with its unquiet ghost.   The Ghost House
was an empty cottage nine miles beyond Benalder
Lodge and fifteen miles from Dalwhinnie, near the
west end of Loch Ericht.   It had been built as a
shooting-lodge in the early days of deer-forests when
sportsmen were content with rougher quarters and
more laborious sport than they would accept now.
Then it became a watcher's house where a man but
recently dead lived for forty-one years and brought
up a large family.   No wilder or more isolated
habitation can easily be imagined.   There is no road
to it; a path along the lochside, an old right-of-way

established by drovers in the past, goes within half a mile of the house but does not touch it. The nearest neighbour is at Corrievarqui Lodge, seven miles away on the other side of Loch Ericht. On the Ghost House side of the loch there is no dwelling at all until one comes to Benalder Lodge. The cottage has the immense desolation of Rannoch Moor in front of it, and behind it the cliffy bulk of Benalder, amongst whose precipices Prince Charlie hid in the days when he fled from Culloden and was hunted everywhere. He had his Cage in Benalder just behind the cottage.

The door of this house used never to be locked. The country round is so wild and dangerous that the house made an essential place of refuge for men overtaken by storm. Many people had found its shelter a boon in the days before the navvies came. They, being accustomed to *scran*,* took the house with its open door as a godsend. The Grampian Power Scheme had great works, with huge camps of men, at both ends of the loch, so that a stream of foot-loose navvies was never done flowing along the old right-of-way from Rannoch to Dalwhinnie and back again. Navvies are a restless race. They are quite happy and settled in their work one day; the next, they lift their books and sling their working-boots across their shoulders and pick up their drummies and depart—in search of the same sort of work, but somewhere else.

* Scrounge.

Ian used to tell me that in the last days of his ghillieing at Benalder it became scarcely safe to be on the path by the loch, for when you were miles out of sight and sound of the world of men, right in the deepest depths of the forest, with nothing around but rock and bog and water, suddenly a tatterdemalion figure with a chocolate box under its arm would spring into view and before you knew what was happening he'd have sold you shoe-laces and collar-studs—surely the pioneers of our shop-keeping race have never sold worthless beads and baubles in any wilderness in the world more bleak and unpromising of sales than these gloomy shores by Loch Ericht, where the narrow only path is overhung by horrid rocks and beaten by the short steep waves of the loch.   It must have been a strange experience to buy a collar-stud one did not want under the cliffs of Cor an Iolair where eagles once nested and now the peregrines scream.

Upon this path a sudden commerce sprang up, a going and coming of tramps and navvies and men going legitimately from one section of the job to another.   Here they met and made small fires which left neat round black marks on the ground, as tidy as if they had been drawn with a compass. Here they lay and talked beside their fires, if any one would listen, about wars they had seen, South African campaigns and forays in the East.

These men made a half-way house of the cottage in Benalder Bay at the west end of the loch until

some malicious old soldier, earning the price of a
pint with his tongue, insinuated that the cottage was
haunted.   He had heard—ah, what had he heard
as he lay sleepless in that dark house; he heard
queer noises that were not the loch lapping nor
sea-piets screaming nor the wind in the rocks nor
any mortal noise of this world.   Other men were
not lacking to remember that they had heard
strange sounds too.   Irish voices murmured that
there were such things as leprechauns and water-
horses.   The tale went snowballing until we heard
it and Ian dressed it up and gave the phantom a
local habitation, a shape, and a name, for a dozen
newspapers.

We were wise correspondents who realized that
people are the more ready to believe an incredible
tale if you make them think they are very sophisticated by giving them cause to doubt another fable.
(People say It must have been a ghost I saw because
I saw it and I don't believe in ghosts.)   There is a
very ancient tradition that the west end of Loch
Ericht was once dry land, the prosperous sinful
parish of Feadail.   The heavens wearied of Feadail's
wickedness and sent a deluge which destroyed it.
The loch covered the parish, but one might still
hear its church bell on still days, tolled by the
movement of the deep restless waters which hid it
for ever; so ran tradition.

Ian pointed out that the Grampian Power Scheme,
by lowering the loch, had disproved this ancient

K

tradition. One might now see the bottom of the loch and nothing was there save level sand. *Our* legend's truth, on the other hand, was vouched for by scores of witnesses. The house was haunted, he went on, by a woman who once took refuge there from a storm. She was storm-stayed until hunger crazed her and she killed and ate her child. She was seen passing through Rannoch so wild-eyed with despair that no one dared to cross her path. Some said she returned to the wastes of Rannoch, driven by remorse, and was lost in the morasses of that place.

The navvies had done their part, we did ours, and Finlay the stalker crowned the tale. A passing navvy asked him for his opinion of the matter.

'The truth of it?' said Finlay, 'how can I tell? What do I know of truth? She went past here with the child, that's truth I know. She had no child when she came to Rannoch, that's truth I've heard. *What happened to the child?*'

Finlay's performance was the more magnificent since he had never heard a whisper of the woman-and-child story until the navvy mentioned it to him as he asked his opinion.

But a ganger arrived who knew not ghosts. Finlay told us how the poor mother was laid at last to rest.

'They're building a pier at Benalder Bay,' he said. 'Beside your Ghost House, Ian.'

'*Your* Ghost House,' Ian corrected him.

'Not to argue about its parentage,' Finlay went on blandly, 'a gang of men went up to build the pier and I heard they were using the house to live in. They're not supposed to do that so I took Danny (his deer-pony) and went along to evict them.

'I had a few things all ready to say,' he continued. 'They knew I was coming and I expected to find them out of the house. Well, they weren't. They were in it, a dozen of them; man, it was the shock of my life; as soon as ever they heard Danny first one came running out, and then another, and then Macleod the ganger with his arms stretched as if he was going to take me into them. "Man," he cries in Gaelic, "this is a happy day, just come right in and don't wait, the kettle's on the boil; oh, man, I've been looking and longing for you."

'And what could a body do then,' asked Finlay, 'but go in and have a cup of tea. You'd enjoy meeting Macleod, Ian, he's a warrior, he's been all over the world in every war since forty years and every row since sixty and that's his age. Left his folk and home in the Hebrides when he was a boy. Never went back. Couldn't bide in one place. Won't be here long. And och Ian, Ian, he's laid your ghost.'

'*Your* ghost,' said Ian.

'I asked him about it,' said Finlay. '"Ghost!" he says, "did you not know I have a brother a Professor in the Free Church? Oh lad, lad, what

with his piety and my unregenerate heart there's
not a ghost on earth nor a devil in hell would share
a house with me. No, lad, I lay ghosts and I scare
devils. Have another droppie tea.'' The tea,'
added Finlay, 'would have laid ghosts by itself.'

An old legend was dispatched, and the new one
did not live long. But the navvies brought even
stranger things than ghosts. They made a change
in the old traditional names of places along the lochside. Benalder Bay was locally known as Cook's
Bay from the name of the watcher who had lived
so many years in the cottage. The local name was
changed by navvies to Cook's Tours, probably
because they enjoyed sailing there from the east
end. Then Camus ton echt suddenly altered to
Tunney's Bay, and Camus na Grain, which a
generation without Gaelic had anglicized to Green
Bay, was renamed Greenock Bay by homesick
Clydesiders. One could see how a country took its
place-names in the days when men were new in it.

Chapter Sixteen

WE EARN A GREAT DEAL OF MONEY

Ian's visit to the navvy encampment on Saturday afternoons was made primarily to pick up passengers. But he took the chance to sell some fruit and vegetables to the men, who were now feeding themselves instead of being fed by the contractors to the Grampian Power Scheme. They bought potatoes and onions but they also had an appetite for fruit and were charmed to let Ian teach them new ways of eating it. I was sad when I missed seeing him surrounded by a whole ring of men busily making holes in oranges, inserting some sugar, and sucking. But he never succeeded in educating them up to grapefruit, or down to bananas.

We usually sold thirty shillingsworth of fruit and vegetables on Saturday afternoon before the taxying began; it was a useful market, but the taxying was the important and profitable business which increased until we could scarcely cope with it all. We were very sorry that we had begun it so late in the summer, when the job along Loch Ericht was already beginning to close down. Yet even as it was, Corybante made two or even three runs to

Dalwhinnie on a Saturday, or sometimes went so
far as Kingussie with men who wanted to spend
one Saturday night farther afield.

Corybante's fame went through the country and
when Ian began to fetch his passengers back from
Dalwhinnie after closing time on Saturday night
half the village stood by to see the fun. Ian began
by shepherding the navvies towards Corybante, into
whose depths he tried to get them to stow themselves peaceably. There was no limit that we ever
discovered to what Corybante would carry or the
navvies suffer rather than be left behind. When
they were packed in layers like herring and hung
over the edge like a load of hay we felt it was a
mercy that the Benalder road was soft if they
tumbled out.

The packing aboard of far too many men amused
the onlookers. The passengers themselves were
generally either past annoyance or so full of themselves as not to care what happened to their limbs.
Some slept placidly through all their sufferings.
They were easy to deal with. It was the hearty,
cheerful fellows who tried Ian's patience. I need
not say that I did not accompany him on these
jaunts. I stayed safe in Benalder or at the caravan
and only learned by hearsay how efficient my
husband became in dealing with noisy, drunk,
quarrelsome, and affectionate navvies.

Getting the men aboard was the worst task. They
came strolling from the hotel as if they had all the

future to do what they liked with. At Ian's peremptory shouts and horn-hootings, they exclaimed with astonishment, 'There's the car!' but hurried their steps not one iota. They would suddenly discover affinities and soul-mates in the middle of the road and halt to clasp each other's hands and slap each other's backs and hang round each other's necks and tell each other their life-histories. At last Ian would have them dragooned on board, and counted; I heard him once make his tally, demanding, 'Hey you, where's your friend, the big bloke who came down with you? Oh, where the devil is that old man with the whisker? Damn it, I'm going!'

Corybante would be full and running over and loaded at last with the final straggler, but as sure as Ian tried to clamber aboard he would find some cheerful imbecile in the driving-seat playing with the controls; when that nuisance was rudely thrust aside there would be a stirring in the carefully built pile behind; a voice would articulate from the depths, 'My parcel!' and the whole edifice of bodies would disintegrate with a whoop of joy as one man galloped to the shop for messages he had forgotten; another felt thirsty and tried to slip back to the hotel; and two or three more got out simply to hold a conversation. If Ian showed impatience because one man did not appear, the entire cargo rose up to hunt for the sinner, getting lost themselves in the process. In the end the only thing to do was to tootle the horn and depart slowly, pursued by a staggering, worried pack.

Fortunately the navvies were biddable, for otherwise Ian could never have driven through the wood. But though he could scold them into lying as quiet as mice for at least ten seconds across his shoulder and round his legs, he had to grope for the gear-lever or the hand-brake, and once travelled a mile in bottom gear because he could not move his arms or hands to get out of it.

The navvies took the trip with all its discomforts and positive dangers completely as a matter of course, and actually seemed to forget that they were on a car. Arguments which began in the pub continued through the journey. Weird theories and scraps of information came drifting to Ian's ears, and all the time that Corybante dipped, splashed, soared, and plunged on that abysmal road the talk soared to heaven and sank into tunnels these men had driven through the depths of the earth; swelled into battle talk and faded into imbecile expressions of amiability and good-will. It was no uncommon thing for a man seated quiet beside Ian to hear a provocative remark from the rear of the car and, turning round, sprawl over his companions to deliver a speech pointed with threats of violence against some other dialectician clinging excitedly to the hood-stays or standing on the spare wheel at the rear. At regular intervals Ian was forced to halt the car. He stood up in his seat and bawled like a bull till there was an approximate silence in which he could describe the virtues of good passengers. His chief difficulty was always in quieting the helpful men who made a pandemonium exhorting their companions to keep their tongues shut, and came to the verge of fighting in an attempt to keep the peace.

We did like the Irishmen who composed the bulk (one cannot speak of a majority in such an inchoate mass) of our passengers. Even their earnest and frequent requests to Ian that he should do them the favour and eternal obligation of stepping out to have a little fight to show that they were all friends together were conceived in a generous spirit. There were occasionally men who made a nuisance of themselves, and had to be threatened with a spanner. One fellow leaned over Ian's shoulder and told him how to drive, until my husband in a rage offered to throw him in the loch and let him walk home. The latter part of the threat was the more effective. The navvies did not love to walk.

Corybante's terrific power was shown on the evening when Ian had just loaded all his passengers on board and was departing from Dalwhinnie. A crowd of men hailed him and begged a lift. Their spokesman said they had come by boat from the west end of the loch and now they must walk all the sixteen miles back unless Ian took them part of the way.

Ian and Corybante were willing. The crowd piled themselves one above another; they stood on

the running-boards, they stood on each other, they
draped themselves across the front wings, there
were twenty-four men, most of them fairly large
men, on Corybante that evening, and she pulled her
load without a murmur through the mud to Benalder.

While our passengers from Benalder were in
Dalwhinnie other navvies from Dalwhinnie hired
us to take them to Newtonmore or Kingussie. We
were never bedded before three o'clock on Sunday
morning. I gave up going away from the caravan
on Saturdays at last. It was always a comfort to
hear Corybante's roar as she swept homeward with
my husband, who gobbled down the porridge and
milk I made for him and said nothing to all my
questions as to how he fared except, 'Oh, my God!
what folk! Oh, my God, what a day!'

Corybante was a miracle, but even she did not
escape scatheless. A sheared pin in her clutch cost
us two pounds and a week-end's hiring. I think
Ian was glad of one week-end away from the
Benalder road. All the same he liked the job, he
liked the navvies, there was no risk of loss as there
was with the fruit—unless he lost his life in Loch
Ericht. The navvies were honest and easy to deal
with if they were treated like children. The
country looked askance at them as it looked at us.
They were none too well fed. They were badly
housed. If they spent the freedom of Dalwhinnie,
which Corybante gave them, drinking too much
beer, it was their own business.

Chapter Seventeen

WE RETURN TO INSTRUCTION

As if we were not already busy and lucky enough with our fruit-hawking and our taxi-driving and our news-corresponding, a fourth job fell into our laps in the last week of July. We were asked to tutor a boy in Newtonmore whose father proposed to send him to Cambridge. Ian taught him what he could remember of his Maths, and I taught him Latin. We took him for an hour on alternate evenings at seven shillings an hour, and since we already required to go to Newtonmore each day to send our weather report, we were two very welcome guineas a week entirely to the good.

Old proverbs about fair-weather friends were very forcibly recalled to us while we were making arrangements to begin this tutoring. We had arranged to interview our future pupil's father at ten o'clock on a Monday morning. But on the Sunday night, as we were returning from Benalder, to which Ian had driven his tradesmen, Corybante ran dry of petrol five miles from Inverton. It was a dark, dirty night with blustery winds and squalls of rain which were, if only we knew it, a foretaste of the weather to come. The spot where Corybante conked out was hopeless for parking. The road was lined with high banks, and since we dared not run the battery down by leaving the lights on all night, and since we could certainly not leave the car lightless on the busy road, the alternatives were to light a fire and stay out all night beside the car or push it until we reached a place where we could turn her off the road.

Ian always had a preference for the more desperate course, so he decided we must push Corybante, though she weighed nearly two tons. And it really was no night for lying out; even the toughest tramps would be under shelter. Ian ran alongside the car pushing and steering as best he could while I heaved from behind. With the wind to aid us we got over a little rise which led to a gentle downhill slope, not sufficient to keep the car rolling by itself, but helpful all the same. We got her off the road at last and walked to the caravan. We were weary and worried too because the Matchless engine was in bits, to which Ian had reduced it in an enthusiastic moment when he expected to have more time to put it together again than he did have. And we had our interview in the morning. We recalled a former class-mate and friend who was living not very far from our camping-place. He had a little car in which he ran about all day, and he might give us a lift to Newtonmore.

We presented ourselves at his door early on

'Ian always had a preference for the more
desperate course.'

the Monday morning. It was a most beautiful morning with the promise of great heat to come. Mist lay in the valley all along the Spey, and rose from the fields and hills; all the world gave off vapours under the rising heat of the sun. We felt very joyful as we walked to our neighbour's house.

He was strangely reticent. When we explained our trouble, and asked him to take us to Newtonmore, he hummed and he hawed. He hadn't had his breakfast yet. We said in haste, but there's no immediate hurry; we don't need to be there till ten o'clock. Oh, he said, ten o'clock, what a pity; there were people coming to visit him, he must meet them in Kingussie without fail. We'd run out of petrol had we, what a pity, it was all a terrible pity, he hadn't even spare petrol, if it'd been anything else we'd asked he'd have done it like a shot. But those people coming, you know, silly people, he'd much rather help us but there it was you see, awfully sorry and what a pity. We'd run out of petrol!

We thought as we walked away that if he had to go to Kingussie in time to fetch people by noon he might have gone by Newtonmore and taken us with him. Well, that was an old class-mate, an old friend indeed, who'd come times without number to my digs in Aberdeen to gossip and drink tea; who'd condescended to come and drink our coffee at the caravan—after it was dark, we remembered with sudden insight. If it had been tramps or tinkers who were stranded we'd have made an effort to do something for them. Of course, we were just waifs like the folk we gave tea to, and for whom Ian mended old motor-bikes and push-bikes.

We walked in a rage to Newtonmore; rage is a wonderful passer of the time. We were very late for the interview, very dusty and very cross, but we were urgently needed, so we got the job. We marched homewards again along Newtonmore's lengthy, dusty, blazing-hot street. All at once our quondam friend appeared with his car round a corner and entered the street in front of us as if to come towards us, but when he saw us he reversed and departed in the opposite direction, back to Inverton. We bought petrol and borrowed a tin to carry it. We had our two guineas after all, in spite of our friend. We began to feel almost charitable. Our request to be taken to Newtonmore must have put terror in his soul; and we had the best of it, because he came to Newtonmore with an empty car and we saw him. He could never face us again.

He has tried to, but I rejoice to say that Ian has snubbed him as viciously as ever he is capable. We walked the five miles to where Corybante lay. The petrol was heavy and the furious sun blazed on us but we were sustained by the last embers of our righteous rage. We said, we've got on all right

without anybody's help and we'll depend on
ourselves in future, we won't ask favours of any
one.   Then we shan't be disappointed and we'll
have our independence to sustain us no matter what
happens.

Chapter Eighteen

WE ARE FULL OF NEWS

That gusty night when Corybante ran dry of petrol
was a prelude to August weather. When July
ended then the summer was done and rain fell and
the rivers rose and everything was cold and clammy.
The van's timber had shrunk with the drought.
Now the pelting rains found their way through
cracks and open seams and ran down the chimney.
But we were far too busy and prosperous to let the
weather make much difference to our arrangements
or our spirits, though even the sale of enormous
loads of fruit and vegetables could not let us view
the flooded waste valley of the Spey, where hay-
ricks bobbed in a waste of muddy water, with any
equanimity. We learned that the back-flooding
from Loch Insh, which had turned all the meadows
between Kingussie and Kincraig into a morass even
in dry weather, and a lake in time of flood, was due
to the silting of the mouth of the loch. A bar of
rock across the river dammed up the mud which
came down from the hills; and the blockage increased every year, sending floods farther and
farther back. The channel could have been cleared;
there was once talk of clearing it and plans were

made for the work.   It would not have cost a great
deal then.   But nothing was done.

'Nothing was done' might be the motto, or perhaps
the epitaph, of the Highlands.   No one cares enough
for this country to devote himself to its reclamation;
no one has cared enough for many a year.   If it
grows grouse and deer and a diminishing number
of sheep, that is good enough.   No one has pride in
the country.   To live in it from day to day, from
hand to mouth, is enough.

We tried to say so in a variety of newspapers,
being foolishly slow to learn that newspapers deal
in news.   It is their job to report and not to reform
the world's doings.   As we slowly took in this
elementary principle we decided that we must be
as businesslike about our news-corresponding as we
imagined ourselves to be about our fruit.   We had
been warned to avoid sales of work and church
socials.   That evasion presented no difficulty; but
there were other social events which it was our duty
to report, sheep-dog trials for instance.

Ian was always finding his conscience as a news-
correspondent at variance with his inclination to
put the world right.   Even the sheep-dog trials at
Kingussie, which we visited specially on purpose to
report their results in the baldest and most news-
papery fashion, made him angry instead of accurate.
To begin with, though he was now quite an efficient
hawker and solicited trade from utter strangers
with very little diffidence, he had an almost un-

conquerable aversion to enquiring into other people's affairs for the purpose of sending them to a news-paper. Our neighbours' dances, deaths, and epi-demics seemed to him their own affair, and this in spite of the fact that we constantly found people to be avid for publicity.

If we had been really good correspondents we should have said 'Press' boldly as we entered the turnstiles to the sheep-dog trials. But we paid our shillings meekly; and I was bored and Ian was infuriated entirely at our own expense.

Then we should have introduced ourselves to the officials and made certain of their getting a list of the prize-winners to us immediately the business was over. Instead, we sat on a sunny hillock and Ian glowered at the dogs and the shepherds until, when the last competitor had done, my unwilling husband drove himself to go to some understrapper of the trials to ask who had won what. It was all very inefficient; if we were going to be reporters we had no business to be shy.

I must say that Ian's obvious disapproval and strident remarks enlivened my afternoon if they pleased no one else. He began by saying sheep-dog trials were a sort of social rammy with all the gentlemen farmers, who were neither gentle-men nor farmers, dressed up like shepherds, except that their crooks and their plus-fours were too long for any shepherd. Then he said that the whole business was silly anyway. *He* had worked a dog

in the Highlands, and if it had tried any of the belly-
creeping, snaking and mooching around which won
prizes at trials he'd have been on the hill yet; he'd
never have got the sheep home. Then he said that
you could easily see how many sheep all over the
country had been mistreated in the weeks before
the trials, when their shepherds, instead of shepherding them, were training their dogs on them.
He carried on in a loud voice to allege that ninety
per cent. of the people present didn't know a
gimmer from a hogg, and how could they have
any interest in seeing dogs work—if you could
call this sort of gymnastics work. What *he* liked
was a dog that went out as fast as it could, gathered
or drove the sheep without any waste of time, lay
down when it was told, and ate brose. To blazes with
poodle-faking. He pointed to a collie which was
watching the dogs at work with the most avid
interest and he said that the brute was the most
intelligent and only interested onlooker he could
see. When people began to regard him unpleasantly my mild husband glowered at them with
obvious hatred and only interrupted his little chat
to cry with delight because one gaunt speedy collie
had gathered the three sheep and brought them
home in a compact group without ever bothering
to halt for one of the little flags he was supposed
to go round.

'That's the sort of dog I like,' quoth Ian. 'It
does its job as fast as it can and no nonsense. Fancy

trying to do a big gathering, fancy trying to bring home a lot of wild old yowes with lambs with one of those belly-scratchers.'

While we were listening to the speeches and making furtive notes one of Ian's relatives discovered us and invited us to tea.

We blush still over our behaviour to this, the most kind and pleasant of Ian's multitudinous Badenoch relatives. We took tea with him and told him that we were living in a caravan. His wife said, 'You poor dears, you must be dying for fresh vegetables. I know what it is to have no garden. You must take some vegetables with you. We have more than we know what to do with.'

The tragedy was that so had we. But we could not refuse without being discourteous or else explaining all about our fruit-hawking. It seemed that these relatives of Ian were not aware of the ignominy he had brought on the name of Macpherson. We returned to Inverton with two cabbages, two turnips, and some raspberries. And there we laid them beside our dozen cabbages which we had foolishly bought from Glasgow, our bag of turnips from Perth, and our stone of green peas.

We bought these cabbages because we were selling so many potatoes and carrots and onions. They cost us threepence each; the carriage on a bag of a dozen was three shillings; and they were huge coarse brutes of things which no one would buy. We threw them out for the sheep to eat at last. The green peas dried up and went likewise to fatten the sheep.

But we sold our hostess's cabbages for twopence each and her turnips for a penny the piece. The thing was done before we realized what we were doing.

The sheep-dog trials were in early August. With the Twelfth of that month we began to find news-getting a thoroughly profitable task. All our news-papers were eager to hear how many grouse were killed on the moors on the Twelfth, and we made several pounds out of it. But one Scottish paper advised us that it would go on paying half a crown for every result of a day's shooting on each moor. Even in that unlet year there were at least a dozen moors in our area, though they did not shoot every day. We rushed through our first day's fruit-selling, gulped down supper, and set out in the evening to call on six or seven gamekeepers and to ask how many grouse had been killed on their ground that day; it earned fifteen shillings or seventeen and six a day.

Ian actually became an employer of labour. He hired spies or informers throughout the country from whom he learned what happened on moors he was too busy to visit, or which were very remote.

The profit was not without pain. The shooting-lodges we visited almost invariably lay at the back of wild hills, at the end of rough stony tracks. By

good fortune we had no difficulty in learning the
results we sought. Gamekeepers came running to
meet us and to tell us with pride how well their
moors had done. They invariably hastened to ask
whether any one had done better on neighbouring
moors. And they were very sad when Ian's bad
writing, or their own inaccuracy, or the telegraph
people, converted 'Lord So and So with three guns'
into 'Lord So and So with four guns'.

If they could not quote a big bag, they tried to
deceive us by saying so many grouse instead of so
many brace in the hope that we would carelessly
take brace for granted. And they did not fail to
say that their best totals were the result of a half-
day's shooting. Likewise they said that on their
moor there were plenty of birds but the sportsmen
could not shoot. On neighbouring moors, now,
there were few birds but the guns never missed.

We found it enchanting, so long as we kept from
thinking of the silly business this commercialized
sport is, to ride through the sweet, dusky country,
over hill, over dale, and at last to come on a gamekeeper in beautifully cut plus-fours, waiting to try
to deceive us. The days were often wild but the
evenings turned fair and the moors were fresh and
lovely. Thus August went down to its busy close.
The rain pelted but the seams of the caravan had
closed and we were snug and warm in it. The
rivers rose and we caught fish. Roads were flooded
but Corybante strode through them with seven-

league boots. Our tutoring went on, our navvies
waited to be taxied, guns blattering amongst the
hills told us to what moors we must ride at night.
The summer waned on our ascending star and all
we touched was successful.

Chapter Nineteen

WE TRY TOO MUCH

Yet from time to time we learned not to be too bold. We were selling so much fruit that we began to grudge the waste of Monday. We decided to make a long journey right outside our territory, taking bedclothes with us and camping the night wherever we arrived. We could take a mattress in the trailer and sleep under the canvas cover. It was all very romantic and daring.

The Monday we chose dawned so bright that we scarcely bothered to notice that the fruit we ordered over the week-end was tashed and jaded. We heaved it aboard Corybante, on top of the mattress and bedding and pots and pans. It began to rain when we went through Aviemore. We spent some time in Carrbridge making vain calls. No one wanted our fruit there. (Villages went strangely by contraries; some, like Insh and Kincraig, were full of customers; some, like Carrbridge and Boat of Garten, would have none of us; we never could understand why there should be these differences; of course a good local shop would cause it.)

I had bought lovely chops for our supper. We made a smoky fire at midday which ruined them.

Rain poured on us and began to soak our bedclothes and the mattress. We got into a rage with each other and went home as fast as we could with all our waste fruit. Our only consolation arrived when we gave a lift to an old woman with a basket in her hand.

She sighed with pleasure as she sat down. Then almost immediately she opened her basket and let out half a dozen tiny chickens on Corybante's floor, amongst the bedclothes.

'Did you see my chickens?' she asked with pride. 'It's little chickens I'm taking to my docther that's married on a man in Aviemore. Aren't they bonny little beasties? They'll be surprised seeing me. They're not expecting me till later but now I'll be earlier thanks to the lift it's very kind of you and if I'd a single penny in my pocket I'd buy something but I haven't a penny on me you can try me and see.'

We said that we believed her; and were the chickens of a special strain?

'Special!' she exclaimed, 'the very best! Their father was a prize-winner at Grantown Show an' they come offa the best 'laying hens in the country though I say it myself as perhaps shouldn't. Ten eggs a day I get from the ten hens I have and if my man was here he'd tell you the same.'

We said good-bye to her in Aviemore with mutual respect. Her cheerfulness helped to restore our spirits. We had merely been over-bold and the weather helped to destroy a plan we should not have made.

'Aren't they bonny little beasties?'

Chapter Twenty

IS A CHAPTER OF ACCIDENTS

All our affairs were going so well that no rain could damp our hopes for long and the minor mishaps that we were able to overcome or remedy served but to strengthen our vain-glory. Alas, in the blundering days that followed we needed all our confidence.

I had to put in a fortnight's teaching before my year was completed and I was free. So in the last week of August we went to Aberdeen on the Matchless, and thence to my place of bondage. It was one of the wettest days of that wet month. The whole world was sodden and miserable under sullen skies and the hills gushed water; every slope was white with exulting torrents whose loud cries were shouts of victory over the prostrate earth. Ian saw me to the door and then returned his weary miles of rain and more rain to reach the caravan, too bruised with wind to cook himself a meal or light a fire.

He wrote me almost every day to report his progress—if one can call it that. It was a sorry tale for the Spey rose each day to new high levels and the entire country was waterlogged. All this ceaseless rain made his rounds dirty and disagreeable

'We went to Aberdeen on the Matchless.'

and there was no one to halve the labour of selling.
Finally he left the trailer at home and stowed all
the fruit into the back of Corybante, making his
rounds like that. The miserable weather affected
his customers and trade grew less and less as the
splashy pools round houses took on a look of per-
manence. There was less gossiping now, there was
less fruit bought even in Lynchat, Kincraig, and
Insh. At last his sales went down to one pound
where they were five. He wrote me dismally—

*I fear the time of fruit-selling is almost at an end.
Of course I still have a few faithful customers of
whom the most faithful is our Irishwoman at Loch
Vaa who is still very concerned about the immensity
of Corybante.*

She had often spoken to both of us about Corybante's cumbrousness and referred to her as 'that
big baste'. Now, actuated by sheer kindliness of
heart, she wanted to sell Ian a much smaller car.
She and her man bought it from a doctor in Elgin
and she besought Ian to come and look at it.

I peered into a shed, his letter went on, *and saw
an old red two-seater lying dormant there. According to its owner* 'shay's the very thing for you.
Forty-five miles to the gallon and more if you're
careful.' *I promised to think it over and went to
Benalder. Finlay says to buy it for him if the
La Ponette—that, believe it or not, is the name of
the car—is any good. I might do a spot of car-
coping. What do you think?*

I was extremely doubtful about Ian's capacity to do a deal, but he was sure he could bring it off. So he gathered Finlay's son and drove back to Loch Vaa. He wrote me again—

—so we brought the La Ponette, which is now called Salome, into the light of day. She's the queerest-looking thing with an erect hood and a projecting rear exactly like a Victorian lady wearing a red flannel petticoat over a bustle and managing to look skittish without showing her legs. Well, we poured in petrol and oil and pumped up the tyres; and believe it or not her engine sang like a kettle at the first swing. You should have seen the look of guile-less pride in our Irishwoman's eyes. She affirms— and I believe her—that Salome'll start like that at any time. We took the car down the road and in spite of your sneers her engine is a miracle. So is her gear-box. You simply can't miss a change, which is a delight after Corybante. Well, I paid four pound ten for her and George drove Corybante home. He acted as pilot and scout because of course the La Ponette wasn't licensed. Now you're going to get your chance to say 'I told you so!' We arrived safely at Inverton, but after I'd made tea for George (and we did wash the dishes) we found that two of the La Ponette's tyres were flat. We mended eight blooming punctures and just as it was getting dark we got off to Dalwhinnie. Then another tyre went phut and since we hadn't any more repairing stuff we'd to fit the spare wheel hoping it would stand up. We got

into Dalwhinnie, and just as I was getting round the
corner at the petrol station on to the Benalder road
Salome pitched forward on her nose.   We hadn't
fixed the spare wheel properly and it came off and
ran about a hundred yards while the car's flywheel
knocked sparks out of the road for there's no ignition
switch and you've got to shut off the petrol and wait
till the carburettor empties.   George and I hunted
for the retaining ring of the wheel which evidently
came unscrewed but we couldn't see a trace of it.
It was pretty dark by now.   There wasn't any more
damage, but Salome's useless till we find the retaining
ring.   We hoiked her off the main road—Corybante
lifted her like a dog lifting a rat before it worries
it—and left her there.

I spent a most uneasy night over Ian and his
Salome.   But worse was to follow.   The taxying
was drawing to an end because the work along Loch
Erichtside and at Benalder was finishing.   The loads
of navvies, though more comfortable, were fewer
and less profitable.   Ian scarcely grudged losing the
trade, because every time he went to Benalder he
felt more angry and unhappy about the conditions
in which the few remaining navvies were living.
The catering firm had gone, taking their stove with
its hot-plates along with them.   The last few work-
men had to cook as best they could on fires made in
the open.   They were living in tents, and anything
more wretched than autumn nights in Benalder
under leaky canvas is difficult to imagine, though

Ian had no difficulty in describing it. Rage lent him words.

The Saturday after Salome's defection he went to Benalder as usual and on the way there ripped a tyre to pieces on a sharp stone. He and his load of men pushed the car to a heap of timber at the roadside and used the logs to jack Corybante up. By the time the spare was fitted every one was mud and grime to the eyes. In the evening he took men to Newtonmore. Half-way to that village Corybante began to make dreadful sounds. There was nothing to do but creep home and wait till morning. Morning convinced him that he had run a big end. On Tuesday I had another letter—

Corybante has run a big end. You never heard such a noise as she made coming through Newtonmore. I had to take the men from the village to Benalder on Sunday. When I got there my petrol ran short so I stayed the night with Finlay. I took the tray off this morning and found a big end gone and one of the con rods bent like a bit of wire. I took out the dud piston etc. complete, I could get home on five cylinders anyway. But when I borrowed petrol from Finlay the damn thing wouldn't start. I tried everything and took everything to bits till at last I said was it really petrol. Finlay said 'Oh, yes', but you know what Finlay is. So in a rage of despair I poured out a gollop of the stuff and put a match to it and it was paraffin. We milked as much petrol from a motor-bike as would fill the carburettor

M

and start the car. I came home knocking and pinking and wondering when the blooming engine would jump right out. I gave a lift to a tramp who alleged he was a South African. He'd been wanting to see the peaks of Sutherland because his father was born in the north, so he came to Scotland. If I'd been less wrought up about Corybante I'd have been able to judge how much truth he was telling—damn little I suppose.

I have bought a crate of twenty-four melons.

It was no wonder I was impatient to get back to Speyside to view the ruins—and the melons.

Chapter Twenty-one

WE RIDE THROUGH RIVERS

Ian came for me when my fortnight was up. He arrived on a wild day of wind and rain, and he was dead-tired after a hundred and fifty miles buffeting and soaking on the Matchless, but there was nothing for it but to turn and set out for Speyside at once. There were floods everywhere, roads flooded and fields flooded; bridges choked with sheaves which had been swept from the fields held us up and forced us to make detours. We counted thirteen water-splashes shallow enough to ride through on the way from Aberdeenshire to Speyside, and besides these the road was flooded so deeply in two other places that we had to turn back and find another route. A motor-lorry lay in the roadway in one flooded place. It was submerged half-way up the cab in a swirling torrent. Men and women were labouring in the fields trying to drag sheaves from the reach of the water. Cattle were being driven through the swollen streams to safety. And the valley of the Spey as we neared home was one vast loch from which trees and the railway line emerged sole vestiges of the comparatively dry land I had left when I went away. We had come into Spey-

side at first amongst fires, and now that our fruit-
hawking was winding itself up we drove through
flood.   We were soaked to the skin and bitterly
cold.   The driving rain had found its way into the
caravan.

We were too tired and miserable even to think
about Ian's melons.   But in the morning they were
there before us, a sort of *memento mori* to our
summer and our fruit-hawking.   If it hadn't been
for them we'd have said What can't be cured must
be put up with.   But there they were, two dozen
of them, unsold, unsaleable, constantly reminding
us that we had sunk money in them; and that our
fruit-hawking was done, finished like the summer.

I asked Ian why he bought them.   He didn't
know; he saw them in a fruit-list and they looked
cheap.   We left them lying under the van until
rats bored into them and ate out all the seeds.   Then
we threw them in the burn.   It was a symbolic
action.   It cut us adrift from our fruit-hawking.
When we let the melons roll down the swollen
burn, like so many bald jaundiced heads, we began
to cut our losses and address ourselves to the future.

We weren't afraid of the future.   It couldn't do
anything much worse than the past fortnight had
done.   We hadn't anything to lose.   Our car was
useless—I should say our *cars*, for Salome still lay at
Dalwhinnie—and our occupations were gone.   We
had no more fruit-hawking to do, the navvies were
away, the tutoring was over.   Only news remained.

'It was a symbolic action.'

We started to go seriously after that and especially after news from deer-forests.

The weather began to improve and September turned into a fine month though snow on the peak of Benalder warned us that this was the north, and winter drew on.

In our wandering we found a retaining ring for Salome's front wheel and sold her to Finlay for six pound ten. The profit on the deal restored Ian's self-respect. He felt we had our feet on the ladder of success again.

Once in our journeyings about the country on the Matchless we called upon the Irishwoman at Loch Vaa.

'Oh, dear me,' she exclaimed when we piled disaster on disaster, telling her our recent mishaps, 'oh, dear me, me, me, poor things that you are, have a cup of tay.'

We stood beside the dying embers of the Pink Fire in her garden and drank tea while she bewailed the tricks Salome played.

'The wickedness of the hissy!' she cried, 'have another cuppie tay, me dears. Oh, the wretch, to think of her doing that on you.'

Now September wore on and shooting-parties went away from the grouse-moors, leaving only the deer-forest reports to keep us busy. We began to sell a few articles as well as news to our papers. That, perhaps, would help us through the winter, whose breath was more chill every day.

HALFWAY HOUSE

HALFWAY HOUSE

Chapter Twenty-two

WE BREAK AND ENTER

There were a great many deer-forests and grouse-moors in western Badenoch, along the head of the Spey and by Loch Laggan, which were too far off to visit while we were busy in August. We took the opportunity of the fine weather in September to go to them. The country was strange to me though Ian knew it of old. Loch Lagganside was warm and sheltered and beautiful; the valley of the Spey towards its head slept in the still bright autumn air. But when midday was past, and the sun began to go down, we could feel the chill of winter.

We made up our minds to find a house as soon as we could. We spoke once or twice to Finlay about the Ghost House. It was doubtful if the proprietor would let it, and even if he would, it was impossibly remote. We must be within reasonable distance of a road, and a post office, for our news and journalizing. But we didn't worry a great deal about finding a house. We could make do with the caravan if we must. And something would turn up. The fine weather made us optimistic. We had been lucky in the past.

Of course we could have rented a house in one
of the villages. We didn't want to live in a village.
We couldn't afford village rents in the broken state
of our fortunes.

We went to Garvamore, near the head of the
Spey, hunting out news about great stags from the
forests, and viewing the place where Ian's people
lived long ago, and as we returned we decided to
visit Dalwhinnie instead of going straight to
Newtonmore with our reports.

The quickest, though not the smoothest, way from
Laggan Bridge to Dalwhinnie is by an old military
road which Wade built over a low spur of boggy
hills. We hastened past Drumgask and Cattlodge
and climbed out of the Spey valley until, three
miles from Laggan and quite out of sight of every
other house in the country, we saw an empty
cottage by the roadside. We came off the Matchless
to look at this isolated dwelling, set so lonely by
itself in a great empty circle of moor with hills
beyond. The door was locked but we found an
unsnibbed window and crept through it, going
from room to room in astonishment that it should
lie desolate and be so well preserved. It had five
rooms, three downstairs and two up. There was
a glory-hole under the stairs and a sizeable landing
at their head. The walls of the downstairs rooms
were all lined with new unstained tongued and
grooved boarding which made them light and
pleasant with an appearance of greater size than

they really had and also made them snug and dry.
The fireplaces in the but-and-ben rooms downstairs
were simply huge holes in the walls. One could
burn tree roots whole in them.

We rushed to Newtonmore to find who owned
the place, and if it was to let. In a few days it was
ours for a year at a rent of a pound a month.

We must furnish it now. We went to Aberdeen
with the trusty Matchless. Like all our recent long
journeys, this, the last wild trek of our year, was
made in rain. We were soaked with torrential rain
but our spirits weren't damped for we had found
a house. We hunted through the sale-rooms and
shops in Aberdeen until we found as much furniture
as we could afford to buy. We bought a bedstead
and two big arm-chairs; the chairs were second-
hand; we bought linoleum, carpets, kitchen chairs,
stuff to make loose-covers for our arm-chairs,
curtains, and pots and pans.

Ian bought an axe, and a three-gallon pot to hang
on the hook in our chimney. He bought a cross-cut
saw and a hammer. Then the money we set aside
for our furnishing was almost done. We had spent
twenty pounds on the little we got. We couldn't
afford to hire a lorry to fetch it from Dalwhinnie
to our house. Corybante must make one more
journey.

Chapter Twenty-three

WE USE CORYBANTE FOR THE LAST TIME

When we came home we took Corybante's battery to a garage to be charged. She was very difficult to start on her five remaining cylinders and we had to push her before the engine fired. Once it did start we kept it going; if it stopped, even pushing might not restart it.

We were forced to forsake the caravan and leave it lying at Inverton. We felt very sad as we closed its windows and nailed them shut against the snow-drift. But Corybante would never pull it now; we doubted if Corybante would ever pull it again. It was going to cost more than we thought she was worth to have spare parts brought from America and put into her. Some time when we had money or another car we would return and fetch the caravan over the hills to the Halfway House.

That was the name of our new home. It lay half-way between Dalwhinnie Hotel and Drumgask Inn, and in the days of the drovers, when sheep and cattle and horses from the Highlands had to go south by road on their feet because there were no railways, our house had been a resting-place where the drovers drank and slept while their beasts lay out on the moor called the Stance.

It was a shebeen until almost the end of last century. Ian's shepherding relatives remembered wild times in the rooms where now we were to stow our precious sticks of furniture.

We emptied the caravan of its contents and heaped them in the back of the car. Then we locked and padlocked the door. We did not want strangers to get into the caravan where we had been so happy. Ian gathered pears from the old wild-pear tree which grew near the road on a brae-face looking towards the sun. He would not look back to wave at the caravan, but I did. It was all the home we had had for many a day and now we were forsaking it as if it was just a convenience to be left aside so soon as its use was done.

The Matchless was tied on at the back of the car with its wheels sitting on the drawbar. We needed all the space we had to carry the furniture which was waiting at Dalwhinnie.

Poor Corybante was no longer the car we knew. Her engine, once so smooth and powerful, ran haltingly with scarcely enough force to pull her on top gear on level road. Ian nursed her along and I knew he was afraid she would never climb the hills, Skep Ruadh and steep Drumlaggan, which lay between Dalwhinnie and the Halfway House. He said in a grim voice before we came to Dal-whinnie, 'We'll never carry our furniture as well as

all the stuff in the back in one journey. We'll have
to get rid of this lot first.'

We stuck on Drumlaggan, the hill near Dalwhinnie, by which the road to our house climbed
steeply to its highest point of over 1300 feet above
sea-level. Ian let the car back to the foot again
to rush the hill, and Corybante just got over the
top. Another ten yards and she wouldn't have
done it.

It was dark and cold before we finished the last
of our three journeys back and fore to Dalwhinnie
for the furniture lying there. On the last trip we
punctured a rear tyre but we couldn't wait to mend
it and we couldn't see to change a wheel. We ran
for four miles on that stony, gravelly, water-bound
road on the rim, making the most dreadful noise.
Poor Corybante! she boiled and clouds of steam
and a spray of hot rusty water flew all over her
bonnet and the windscreen. Ian ran her into a
grassy bay at the roadside near the house. She
moved no more out of that until hawkers from
Glasgow offered us thirteen shillings for her at a
time when we were so poor that thirteen shillings
seemed a windfall. We sold her and she was towed
away by a Model T Ford tourer, and that was the
last of our faithful car.

Our home began to take shape and we were
settled down in it by the end of the first week in
October. Ian caught a pound trout in the burn
across the road, which endeared the place to him

for ever. He began to dig fir-roots from the moss and the roots of fallen trees from the wood on the other side of the road from our house, making preparations for winter with its blasts. We stored our fuel in a great heap. The feet of winter were already on the hills, whose peaks were white on many a morning. But round us the sun was bright and warm still, a golden light shone, cock-grouse exulted from their hillocks and stags roared in the forests.

People began to tell us that the road past our house was often blocked for months on end with snow, even into May. We did not heed their warnings much. We were very busy putting our rooms in order and planning how we would make a garden in the moor.

We used the varnish and the stain which we had brought with us from Aberdeen when we came first of all into Speyside, to varnish the floor of the east room downstairs; we made it our living-room. The other room was the kitchen. (I am very very proud of our floor. I've polished it until it shines.) As we had a little money to spare we spent it on paint and distemper. We white-papered the roofs of our downstairs rooms over the rafters, a devilish job for the rafters had been cut from local wood and built into the house when they were damp so that they warped and twisted. They had never been dressed after they left the saw. There was still bark on some of them. But the white paper made

the rooms light and gave the impression of height
although the roofs were low.

The windows were small, and upstairs there were
only skylights. The rooms upstairs were right
under the roof with walls sloping to a peak. We
distempered them.

But our windows looked north, into that airt's
steady light, upon a magnificent scene of wild hills
and country where no house and scarcely a trace of
men's handiwork was visible. The distant soaring
Monadhliaths with their peaks in cloud or snow gave
the view a satisfyingness and one could see it daily
day without growing weary or finding it the same.

But this country which surrounds us is never the
same for many hours together, even when all
circumstances that affect it seem constant. A trick
of the light in this high land makes every moment
alter and each hour show something new.

So our first winter went past, and when it was
done we took a lease of the house for other five years
at a rent of three pounds a year.

That first winter was the hardest we have felt
since we came to Halfway House. When October
ended it grew too cold and wintry to let me do my
washings any longer at the burnside, boiling Ian's
dearly-loved big pot, full of clothes, on a fireplace
he built, over a raging fire of fir-roots. The water
of our burn was the best I have ever found for
washing things clean. It took dirt out like magic,
and when we have come home from a town, weary

with noise and fog and mucky air, we wash ourselves and are like new people.

The cars which passed began to grow few, and then there were none, there were no passers-by except stray folk, tramps and navvies and men looking for work, whose drummies we boiled. We saw one wayfarer come at dawn of a frosty November day to the wood beside us. It was not much of a wood, a hundred or so trees thinly scattered over two hillocks. And the gales of each winter blew down trees for us to burn so that the wood grew steadily less.

Something wakened us very early on the morning when this stranger came to our wood. We looked out at the back skylight to see him light a fire and put a Mackintosh's toffee tin full of water on it. In a little he stripped himself to the waist and began to wash his shirt in the water he boiled. He tied a string between two trees and hung his shirt and a few pairs of socks on this clothes-line. The wind was like ice but he sat on the verge of the burn, naked to the waist, waiting for his shirt to dry. Then he went away and we saw him stride over the hill out of sight.

There were many tramps at our door even in the dead of winter. They told us about themselves as they drank the tea we boiled for them (they insisted on its being *boiled*). There was Jimmy M'Manus from Donegal who would have gone to America instead of coming to Scotland if it weren't that two

N

of his aunts were in America before him. 'And
that's plenty M'Manuses in the wan place,' said he.
And then, '*Oh, what would me mother say to see her
son now!*'

'The owld dog for the hard road,' said one hardy
wayfarer when we wondered at his fortitude, 'the
puppy takes the pavement.' There was something
gallant about these hardened travellers. But there
were also waifs and strays and the broken men of
our industrial civilization, decent working-men on
borrowed push-bikes looking everywhere for the
work they could not find anywhere.

In the very dead of winter, when a blizzard was
raging, a man with his cap on the side of his face
to keep the drift from cutting him came asking us
to boil his drum. His shirt was open and his chest
bare almost to the waist. He was walking on his
heels because his feet were in pain. But he went
away whistling with his hands in his pockets,
shuffling through the snow-wreaths to Dalwhinnie.

The road was blocked for twelve weeks, when not
a car or even cart came through. Ian was walking
home from Dalwhinnie one night during this time.
A gale blew and the night was dark. He walked
off the road, over the fence which was hid deep in
snow, out on to the moor where three women are
said to have gone lost on separate occasions within
recent times, wandering as he did. But a blink
of moonlight rescued him.

The snow packed so hard at last that we could

'And hung his shirt on the clothes-line.'

take the motor-bike over it and tow a sledge laden with two hundredweights of provisions behind the Matchless from Dalwhinnie.

The frost was like iron. We broke ice on our burn with our axe before we could draw drinking and washing water. We spent five hours walking the three miles from Laggan Bridge in a storm which blocked the railway and held up three trains between Drumochter and Newtonmore. We were laden with provisions because the storm came on us suddenly when we were unprepared and had no food in the house. I trudged at Ian's heels, waist-deep in snow, seeing nothing but his back and the howling drift. I had a bag of eggs in my hand which I carried safely all the way until I fell and broke them at the door of our house.

Mice came from no one knows where to keep us company. Spring brought back the birds, peewits and curlews and gulls, to nest, but besides these moorland creatures we had a blackbird, and a chaffinch once; a robin and house-martins which nested under our eaves until a sparrow-hawk ate their young ones when they were starting to fly. Eagles appeared too, and wild swans whooping their melancholy call. We heard ravens amongst the rocks above Loch Coulter. Deer came to our fir wood and roe-deer ate our cabbages when we made a garden. Sheep with their lambs brought spring and nibbled the tea-leaves and potato-peelings we threw out on the moor.

We couldn't afford to buy coals even if we could have got them over the blocked road. We burned roots and blocks of fallen trees, filling the chimney with them to keep out the storm. Bog-fir blazed like the sun itself, filling our huge fireplaces with gouts of smoke and yellow flame, roaring to deafen the very storm. We sometimes had such fires that the chimney caught and we ran outside into the wild night to see the snow illumined by flames which belched from the chimney-top.

When spring came delicately upon the wintry land we began to plan our garden. There was no soil for it, nothing but peat. We bought wire and fenced in a piece of land in front of the house, using split tree-trunks from the wood for posts. Ian made a shed of backs he bought for a few shillings from the sawmill in Benalder. He built a carriage-way from the road into the shed, sweeping round in front of the house. We made a pavement in front of the house with flags and flat stones from the burn and we gravelled our brief drive. When that was done we could keep our feet dry when we went out of doors. Then Ian dug the turf from the road he made, and all the scrapings he could get from the main road, into the peat of our garden. We made flower-beds and we put down potatoes and cabbages. We grew several hundredweights of potatoes and two or three barrow-loads of turnips yearly, as well as cabbages and cauliflowers and kale and brussels sprouts and peas in our patch of garden. We had

to dig out stones weighing three or four hundredweights before we could plant anything. Ian
wanted to make a dry-stone dike with these stones,
but I was so proud of the part I played in levering
them from the ground that I would not let him. I
preferred to have them lying outside our fence as
evidence of what I helped to do. The peat of our
garden became so dry in summer that once it went
on fire when Ian flung a match on it. Sheep found
their way in and almost broke our hearts with grief
when we saw our work ruined. We had spent days
carrying water from the burn to our parched plants
and then a steeple-chasing brute of a sheep made
waste of our labour. But we put down fresh seeds
and plants and they grew again.

The motor-cycle had accidents which forced us to
walk the long weary miles to shop and post office
and station, three miles to the post office at Laggan
Bridge, five miles to the station at Dalwhinnie. We
bought milk and eggs from our nearest neighbours
at Cattlodge. We went to uproarious dances at
Dalwhinnie and came home with the dawn. We
were never so wise and careful of our money as
experience should have taught us to be.

Ian fished and dug peats and I set them up to dry
or tied a rope to the wheel-barrow we *won* so that
I could help to carry them home. People in cars
enraged us by stealing peats from the top of our
stack, letting the rain in. The noise of winds and
burns wakened us and was our lullaby. Sheep

'Tied a rope to the wheel-barrow . . . so that I
could help to carry them home.'

with their lambs paid us morning calls. We had no rich neighbours to make us feel our poverty. The deer and the wild birds were as poor as we. These neighbours, like ourselves, had few possessions. Like ourselves they bore winter patiently because they must; they waited like us for spring. We were alone in country where we felt happy and at home, the kingdom of the beasts around us had no golden key to its gates, and we could look on poverty in idleness without terror.

Chapter Twenty-four

WE SHOULD HAVE STAYED AT HOME

When golden summer came, ambition began to
revive in Ian. He decided that it was not good
enough for us to sit still in the remote moors sending
some news, and some articles, to his increasing
number of papers. He decided to run a shooting-
gallery and to travel with it from one navvy encampment to another throughout the entire Highlands. Well, it's an old story now but bitter even
yet. It cost us more than a hundred pounds and a
whole summer and we went into debt over it. Ian
discovered that he could not raise the money he
needed without security, and the Matchless was
not security except in hire-purchase. So he sold it
to a hire-purchase company for £25 and bought it
back again at so much a month. It was an ingenious
scheme since the bike never left our possession. I
only wish it had been devoted to a more sensible
end. Our shooting-gallery cost us a hundred
pounds besides endless worry and labour and hard-
ship; it cost us miserable nights without any sleep
when we lay in holes and corners of the country
beside unlicensed cars with no lights, waiting for

dawn to light us home while there were no
policemen about.

We ran for one night only and then the last of
the many cars we bought burst up. It was an old
Ford ton lorry and it ran a big end at Kinloch-
Rannoch. Of course it wasn't licensed and of course
we had to slink and hide and sleep in the heather
till we got back to the wilds of Badenoch. We spent
more than a hundred bitterly-earned pounds and
we drew four and sixpence! We were left stranded,
with the caravan in one corner of the Highlands,
our booth in another, our lorry in a third. All we
had for our money was exasperation, four and sixpence, and a few rubbishy prizes we bought and
paid good money for; we had four air-guns which
tramps stole from the caravan while it lay defence-
less. We had a sharp lesson and debts galore. We
went home to the Halfway to lick our deep wounds.

It was a place where wounds soon healed. But
that escapade had repercussions for many a long
day. I shall never forget the miseries of the sad
summer; sitting in the rain beside the car called a
Brasier which Ian tried to sneak out of Aberdeen
at midnight without lights, licence, or insurance;
wondering dreamily if the Aberdeen policeman who
blew his whistle to stop us had taken our number;
gazing through a gray cold dawn at the lighthouse
to which Ian had piloted the Brasier, thinking all
the time he was on the road to Stonehaven; sleeping
in that same Brasier near Blairgowrie, with no

petrol and no money; spending a cold, blustery, wet September night on an iron seat outside Pitlochry; seeing the roadman, and the road surveyor, and the A.A. scout, and the policeman from Dalwhinnie, come in relays to the door of the Halfway with news that the caravan had been blown over in the night and was blocking the Great North Road; watching Ian with half a dozen of his Dalwhinnie friends pull the battered caravan on to its wheels again and then drink whisky from Ian's bottle out of an egg-cup while the blocked stream of traffic raged by.

And to this day Ian says If only this or that had happened, if only we had had money to buy a decent lorry—if only he had repaired the Chalmers and used Corybante for the work—then our shooting-gallery would have made our fortunes.

He has just seduced his friend George into starting to collect and sell the old scrap iron and copper and aluminium which is lying round Dalwhinnie, so I suppose there's no hope of my ever persuading him about the shooting-gallery.

But his dearest plan is to start a market-garden in the Highlands, to sell fruit and vegetables and flowers to hotels and boarding-houses and private homes along the Spey. Perhaps if we can come on a little farm or croft we shall do that yet. But that would mean leaving the Halfway.

I'll make sure we have enough capital for our next folly.

Chapter Twenty-five

WE REMEMBER BEATIFIC SUMMER

Or was it folly? I don't know—I don't care. If we did descend to depths of gloom, we always escaped. And when I remember the days when I taught and Ian corrected exam. papers, I'm ready to feel happy even about the shooting-gallery.

But the shooting-gallery's another story; it and our stay in the Halfway are too long a matter to append like an afterthought to the simple annals of our fruit-hawking.

Our fruit-hawking was successful. It brought us out of jobs we did not like, out of a town, into country where we are at home. We know now that we could never have lived happily in any town or city. We could never go back to live in a city for long. We have given hostages to the country and it is our home.

We sold fruit to people who wanted fruit. We sold the best we could get as cheaply as we could afford. We salved our self-respect by being of use. We were happy.

We were happy because we succeeded. We had never sold anything in our lives before, but we succeeded. There is always that consolation in

'Our garden growing.'

every untoward circumstance.   We earned our
own way.

We were happy in the country which we served
usefully. We were happy because the sun shone
on us and rain soaked us, because winds blew us
about and water cleaned us.   We were happy
because we had white streams to bathe in and we
found a house alone by itself without company in
the wild centre of the moors.   We were happy
because we met fine folk, and men were courteous
—navvies and gamekeepers and tourists too. Oh,
we have many things that make us happy when we
recall them, men gossiping from the tops of haystacks, chickens running about on Corybante's floor,
women washing clothes under high waterfalls, our
garden growing and its penny packets of flower
seeds making a splash of colour in the moor, the
snow drifting like volcanic smoke, white snow black
against the sky on the ridges of the hills.

I wonder what we should have to recall and look
back on if we had been good, respectable people
and stayed in jobs we disliked?   But we did not
stay, and we were not respectable, and we were
happy, in spite of the shooting-gallery.